Ultimate SUDOKU Compendium

igloobooks

Published in 2016
by Igloo Books Ltd
Cottage Farm
Sywell
NN6 0BJ
www.igloobooks.com

GUA006 0716
2 4 6 8 10 9 7 5 3 1
ISBN 978-1-78557-493-1

Cover designed by Nicholas Gage

Puzzle compilation, typesetting and design by:
Clarity Media Ltd, http://www.clarity-media.co.uk

Printed and manufactured in China

Contents

Sudoku is a logic puzzle with simple rules. As such, it requires no knowledge of maths or mathematical ability. Although the puzzle contains numbers, these could be replaced with symbols of any sort as the numbers do not have any mathematical function.

Here is what a standard sudoku puzzle looks like:

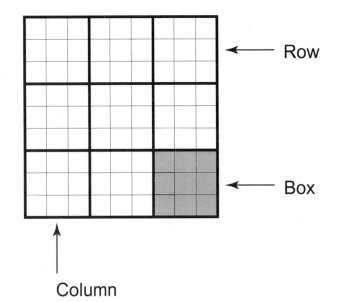

← Row

← Box

↑
Column

The aim of sudoku is straightforward: you must place each number from 1–9 exactly once into each of the rows, columns and boxes in the puzzle grid. The diagram above illustrates one row, one column and one box in the grid.

You will notice that each of these rows, columns and boxes – which are called 'regions' – contain 9 cells. In total there are 27 regions in the puzzle.

At the start of the puzzle, some numbers are already placed in the grid. The aim of the puzzle is simply to complete the puzzle by deducing which number must be placed in each of the empty cells in the grid.

There is only one solution, and it can be reached through logic alone – no guessing is ever required to solve any of the sudoku puzzles in this book.

Sudoku

Puzzle 1   Easy

9	5	4	2	6	3	7	1	8
7	3	2	1	4	8	6	9	5
1	6	8	9	7	5	2	4	3
2	8	9	7	5	6	4	3	1
6	7	5	3	1	4	8	2	9
4	1	3	8	2	9	5	7	6
3	4	6	5	9	7	1	8	2
8	2	7	6	3	1	9	5	4
5	9	1	4	8	2	3	6	7

Puzzle 2   Easy

8	1	6	9	3	7	2	4	5
4	2	9	6	5	1	7	8	3
5	7	3	2	8	4	9	1	6
1	5	7	8	4	9	6	3	2
9	6	2	1	7	3	8	5	4
3	8	4	5	2	6	1	9	7
6	3	8	4	1	2	5	7	9
7	9	5	3	6	8	4	2	1
2	4	1	7	9	5	3	6	8

Puzzle 3   Easy

		6	5		3		1	
			6	1	9	3		8
				7				
	6	5				4		
	9	8	7		4	5	2	
		4				8	7	
			4					
4		9	3	6	8			
	3		2		5	9		

Puzzle 4   Easy

	7	4	5	1				
2	5							1
1	9				6		4	
	3	2	8	5				
			2		9			
				6	1	2	8	
	1		6				5	9
9							2	3
				4	5	1	6	

Puzzle 5   Easy

1								
		7		8			3	
6	8	9	3		4		7	
	9	3	2	6		7	4	
	4	8		7	3	6	1	
	1		8		7	9	5	2
	7			2		3		
								7

Puzzle 6   Easy

5		3		7				
8	9		2	5				
	6				9			
	3	5	6	9				4
6			7		4			9
4				1	2	6	3	
			3				1	
				4	7		9	6
				6		2		3

Puzzle 7   Easy

6	3				2			5
		5						
9		4		1		7	6	2
	2	3	1	9				
	6						8	
			5	6		1	2	
8	9	2		3		4		6
						2		
4			2				1	8

Puzzle 8   Easy

	3	5	1			9		6
	4				6			
6		7	5	2	9			
	7			9		1		
4								3
		2		7			9	
			2	4	7	8		9
			8				6	
8		4			1	2	3	

Sudoku

Puzzle 9   Easy

	7		1	8	6	2	3	
		2					9	
	4				2	7		1
9		7		3	8			
			9	2		6		8
7		5	8				4	
	9					1		
	1	4	2	7	3		6	

Puzzle 10   Easy

2				7		8		9
1	4				2		7	
7			3		9			
	9					6		
	2	6	1		8	9	5	
		7					3	
			4		7			2
	1		2				9	3
9		2		3				6

Puzzle 11 Easy

		1				8		
8			7	6				
9			2	1		6		4
	6	3		9				1
		9	1		6	7		
5				7		9	6	
3		2		8	7			6
				2	9			8
		8				2		

Puzzle 12 Easy

		8		5		3		9
				9				4
		9	3				5	8
		7			4		9	
8	5	1				4	3	7
	4		8			5		
1	8				7	9		
2				8				
7		3		2		1		

Sudoku

Puzzle 13   Easy

				9		2		6
3				1	6		4	9
			5		2	8	3	
							2	8
	9		6		1		7	
8	4							
	6	8	2		3			
7	3		8	5				2
5		9		6				

Puzzle 14   Easy

		7				2	6	4
	1	2			7		8	
					8	9		7
	7		1	2			3	
		8				7		
	6			7	9		4	
9		1	3					
	3		7			8	9	
7	8	6				4		

Puzzle 15 Easy

2	8				1	7	5	
7	1	3					2	
		5		2			1	
			1	9	4			
		9				6		
			5	3	6			
	5			1		8		
	4					5	9	1
	9	1	8				6	7

Puzzle 16 Easy

	5		3			8		
				8				1
	3	1		2	6		4	9
	7		8			4		3
		8				2		
3		2			1		7	
5	8		2	7		1	6	
7				6				
		3			4		8	

Sudoku

Puzzle 17   Easy

4		5		3				
			9			6	4	5
9		6			8		2	
				1	7			2
8		1				9		7
2			6	9				
	5		1			2		4
6	8	9			2			
				8		7		6

Puzzle 18   Easy

	4			8			7	
8		7				9		6
5	6		9			3		
	7			9	2	6		5
9		6	3	1			2	
		8			1		6	3
4		3				7		1
	1			3			8	

13

Sudoku

Puzzle 19 — Easy

9	7		8	4		5	2	3
		4				8		
				5			7	4
	9			8	4		1	
	8		3	1			5	
5	3			7				
		6				1		
7	1	2		6	8		3	5

Puzzle 20 — Easy

1			7		4	2		
4			5	2			1	
		7			1	4		
				4		9	8	2
			3		2			
8	1	2		5				
		9	4			5		
	7			9	8			1
		1	2		5			4

Sudoku

Puzzle 21 — Easy

7				4				
			1	6	5			7
		4			7	9		1
	8		7				2	
3		9	4		6	7		8
	7				8		9	
1		5	3			4		
9			5	7	4			
				1				2

Puzzle 22 — Easy

6	8	3	2					
	5	4	1				2	
		1			5		3	
1	4		6	2				
		6				2		
				8	1		6	5
	1		5			6		
	3				6	7	1	
					3	5	8	2

Puzzle 23 — Easy

	5				8	3		7
		7		3	6		1	
			4			5	6	
	6	8	9			7		
		3				9		
		9			3	2	5	
	8	2			4			
	7		3	6		4		
3			6	8			7	

Puzzle 24 — Easy

5				6			3	
3		7		9	4		1	5
2	9							
	5		6			4	2	
4								1
	1	9			8		5	
							9	8
1	8		9	3		5		4
	7			8				3

Sudoku

Puzzle 25 — Easy

					1	2	5	
		9						3
	6			8				4
7	3		5	2			6	
6		8	4		9	3		2
	9			7	3		4	5
1				5			9	
9						4		
	2	6	1					

Puzzle 26 — Easy

4			3	6				
	3			2	8	4		7
		8			7			
6							4	8
8	5		2		1		7	6
1	4							2
			7			9		
7		5	1	3			8	
				8	2			5

Puzzle 27 Easy

					3			
8			5	2	7	4		
		2		9	4			6
2	4	1				7		
	3	8				9	1	
		7				6	4	3
1			3	5		2		
		5	7	4	1			8
			8					

Puzzle 28 Easy

				9				
	4	9	1		8	7		
	1	8	7		4		6	
1	6					2		
	2	5				3	8	
		7					9	1
	3		2		6	8	1	
		6	4		1	5	7	
				7				

Sudoku

Puzzle 29 — Easy

2	1		9					8
		3	5					
4				3		9	1	
6	8	7		9			2	
		2				6		
	4			5		3	8	7
	6	4		2				1
					5	4		
1					4		9	3

Puzzle 30 — Easy

7				2		1		8
	6				8		3	
8				1			9	7
		2		8	7		1	9
6	1		9	4		7		
3	7			9				5
	9		8				4	
2		6		3				1

Puzzle 31   Easy

4	3	1	8	7				
6					4			
	7	2			1		3	
		6	5			3		
3	2						4	5
		5			9	6		
	8		4			2	9	
			9					1
				8	7	5	6	4

Puzzle 32   Easy

			4				2	
	4					8	9	6
	2			9				4
		2		5	7			9
6	7		9		2		4	3
9			8	3		2		
3				4			7	
7	1	4					3	
	9				8			

Puzzle 33   Easy

		1		4				
4			9		5			8
9		7		3	8	4	6	
	2		5	9				
5								4
				7	3		2	
	4	8	3	5		6		7
1			8		7			5
				6		8		

Puzzle 34   Easy

	7	2	3	4				
3	5						7	1
8		9						
2	1	3	5	9				
			4		2			
				3	7	1	5	2
						4		3
6	3						9	7
			2	3	6	8		

Puzzle 35 Easy

	9				4			3
			6				4	9
6		3	7		9			5
		7			3		8	
	5	6				4	1	
	8		4			3		
1			3		6	5		8
5	6				7			
9			2				6	

Puzzle 36 Easy

5			3			9	4	
	3				8			
6	8		7		4		1	
	2		4		5		8	9
9	4		2		7		5	
	6		8		1		3	2
			5				6	
	5	1			2			4

Sudoku

Puzzle 37 Easy

	6	8			3	1		
	9				6	5		
	4	2		9				
	3		6			4		
4		1	9		5	6		3
		5			8		1	
				2		9	5	
		6	3				4	
		4	8			3	7	

Puzzle 38 Easy

						2		1
			2	1	9			
5		1	7		8			
1			6			3		9
7	9		1		4		2	8
4		2			5			7
			8		6	7		5
			3	5	7			
9		7						

Sudoku

Puzzle 39   Easy

4				8		1	7	9
5		8		2				
1	9							
			8	7		3	9	
3			5		6			1
	8	9		1	2			
							6	3
				3		9		7
9	3	5		6				2

Puzzle 40   Easy

7	2			8				3
			5		7	9		2
	8	4		2				
2	9	8						
		3	7		8	5		
						1	9	8
				1		3	6	
3		6	2		5			
9				6			4	5

Sudoku

Puzzle 41   Easy

5		1	4		8	6		
		8					5	
	6	4		2	9	8		1
		5			2			9
4			6			3		
9		3	2	6		5	4	
	5					2		
		6	1		5	9		3

Puzzle 42   Easy

		3					4	
9	2	5					3	
	4				9	5		2
4			8	9			1	
7			3		6			8
	8			1	5			4
5		8	4				7	
	6					3	8	5
	3					4		

Sudoku

Puzzle 43 — Easy

						2		3
			7		6		8	
8				5	3	6		1
2	3	6	8			9		
			2		5			
		1			7	4	6	2
9		5	3	8				6
	1		6		9			
3		2						

Puzzle 44 — Easy

1		6		7		4	9	
	9	7	5	6				
					9		7	
	4			5	2	6		7
2		8	3	9			4	
	1		9					
				3	5	2	6	
	5	2		4		9		3

Sudoku

Puzzle 45 — Easy

					7	3		8
	8			2			6	7
		3			6	4	2	
1					9	5		
	3	2				9	8	
		7	2					3
	1	6	3			8		
3	7			9			4	
8		4	6					

Puzzle 46 — Easy

						5	9	
		3		5	6			4
8	5		4					3
				4	5		6	1
	7	6				8	4	
4	9		6	2				
3					4		2	9
9			8	3		4		
	6	4						

Sudoku

Puzzle 47 Easy

2		7						5
6	3			5	7		9	
4		9			2		8	7
				3	8			
7								8
			4	9				
9	7		6			8		4
	8		2	4			7	9
3						2		1

Puzzle 48 Easy

1	8				2			5
			9	1			8	4
			3		8			
3		9				1	4	
	4		1		3		6	
	2	1				7		3
			6		9			
9	7			4	1			
4			2				9	6

28

Puzzle 49 — Easy

		2					1	
9		4	2	3		5		
				7	1	4		
	3			2	4		6	
2		7				1		3
	5		3	1			4	
		3	1	6				
		6		5	9	3		4
	9					6		

Puzzle 50 — Easy

			7	1			3	
8				9			4	
	7		4			1		6
4	1					3	5	
7	3						6	9
	9	8					1	4
3		6			4		9	
	8			2				3
	4			3	9			

Puzzle 51   Easy

	3		1		4		5	
		1		3	6			4
7	9			5		3		
	4	7	3		9			
			5		8	9	4	
		5		6			9	8
1			4	8		2		
	2		7		3		1	

Puzzle 52   Easy

5				6				
7			3			6		
	6	3	5			1		
	5		4			7		6
1		8	6		2	5		9
9		6			3		4	
		9			5	3	1	
		5			1			7
				3				2

Sudoku

Puzzle 53 — Easy

	7	1	3			5	8	
	3		2					7
2		8			7			
		6		4		2	1	
3								5
	1	5		3		8		
			5			1		8
8					6		5	
	5	9			8	3	2	

Puzzle 54 — Easy

4			7			5	2	
9		1	5		4	3		
	5					6	9	
				3	8		1	
			4		7			
	3		9	1				
	4	7					5	
		6	1		5	7		3
	8	5			9			2

31

Puzzle 55 Easy

		8				6		9
	7	2		9				
		9		5	8			
	2	3		4	5		8	
		5	1		6	3		
	8		9	2		5	4	
			5	1		8		
				7		9	1	
1		4				7		

Puzzle 56 Easy

	8			1		4		9
		1	2	4	9		7	
	3	4			5			6
1	6		9		4		3	5
9			1			8	4	
	2		7	9	1	6		
8		7		5			9	

Puzzle 57 Easy

	7						9	2
2			9					
	5	9		4		3	1	
	9					2	8	4
		7	4		2	5		
5	4	2					7	
	2	6		1		7	3	
					7			6
7	3						4	

Puzzle 58 Easy

6			1		4	3	2	9
			3	9		6		
	4		2					
	2		6	3			9	
3								7
	7			2	9		3	
					8		4	
		2		6	3			
5	1	8	7		2			3

Sudoku

Puzzle 59 — Easy

2			1			4	6	
				7	6			9
	9		4					7
		8		9			5	1
	4	5				9	8	
9	6			1		7		
4					7		9	
8			9	4				
	7	9			2			6

Puzzle 60 — Easy

	7		6	9	2	8		5
8			4		7		9	
		3					6	
		8	7					2
	6						7	
3					8	5		
	8						1	
	3		1		5			6
5		4	8	7	6		2	

34

Sudoku

Puzzle 61   Easy

9				2	3			1
	2	4	1		6		3	5
			9	7				
			3			4	2	
4								3
	3	9			8			
				5	2			
2	9		6			4	1	8
6			8	9				2

Puzzle 62   Easy

	6			8				
7				5		8	1	
		5	2	4			6	
	3		5				8	
1		7	9		3	4		6
	5				4		3	
	7			1	2	3		
	9	8		3				7
				9			2	

Puzzle 63 Easy

				7			8	4
8		1			2	5	7	
7	4				8			2
					7	2	3	6
6	8	2	5					
4			8				2	7
	3	8	7			4		1
5	6			1				

Puzzle 64 Easy

	8					3		
3		1	9				8	
9			5		8		2	
				4	9			
6	9	5	3		7	2	4	1
			6	5				
	7		8		5			2
	1				2	8		3
		9					1	

Sudoku

Puzzle 65 — Easy

1			3		2		8	
	5		4	8				
					5	2		3
	4		5			8	2	7
		1				6		
7	3	8			6		4	
8		5	6					
				2	7		5	
	7		8		3			6

Puzzle 66 — Easy

					3		8	
			1		8		9	7
	1	9			6	5		
3							5	1
6		5	8		1	3		2
1	4							9
		4	3			7	6	
9	5		6		4			
	3		5					

Sudoku

Puzzle 67 Easy

2		7						8
							6	
3	6	8	1	7		4		
		5		1		6		7
	7		9		5		4	
4		1		6		5		
		3		4	1	8	5	6
	8							
7						2		1

Puzzle 68 Easy

							1	
1	5	9			2	6	7	
		8	9	1		2		
	4				1	5		2
	2						3	
5		7	2				6	
		2		7	6	1		
	9	5	1			4	2	7
	8							

Sudoku

		9				2		4
	4	7			2			1
2			1		4			
3	7	8	4		9			
			2		8			
			3		5	6	9	8
			8		6			3
6			9			7	4	
1		2				9		

		9	3		8	2		7
3		5	4					8
		8						1
1	9	2	6					
			2		5			
					1	3	2	6
8						6		
7					2	1		3
9		1	8		6	5		

Puzzle 71 Easy

	9		1	2		4	3	
					7			
5		2		3		9		
4		7	2	8	6			3
8			3	7	1	2		4
		3		1		8		5
			7					
	1	5		4	3		7	

Puzzle 72 Easy

		1	5		3	9		
		9		7				
		5	1		6			4
5			8	3		7	4	
	9						3	
	2	3		4	7			5
9			7		4	5		
				1		3		
		2	3		5	4		

Sudoku

Puzzle 73 — Easy

				9		6		
	3	9			5	2		1
	1	8						
3	4		9		2		6	
		1	3		7	9		
	9		6		4		1	3
						4	2	
2		3	4			7	9	
		4		7				

Puzzle 74 — Easy

6		5	1			4		
	3			8				6
	7			4			2	5
			8	2			1	
	8		6		7		4	
	6			1	4			
2	1			5			6	
8				6			5	
		6			1	2		3

Sudoku

Puzzle 75   Easy

	9			5		1		
		3	7	9		5	6	
				8		2		9
9	8		2					5
		7				8		
3					5		9	7
4		6		2				
	3	8		1	9	7		
		9		6			5	

Puzzle 76   Easy

4	5					2		3
	2	3	4		7	8		
				3		9		
				3		7		2
		2	6		4	1		
5		7		1				
	6		1					
		5	7		6	9	8	
7		8					2	6

Sudoku

Puzzle 77 — Easy

8	7			5		2		1
			8					
4				3		7	9	
	4	1		7		6		
		6	2		4	5		
		7		6		1	8	
	9	8		2				6
					6			
6		4		8			2	7

Puzzle 78 — Easy

		5			2	7		1
		9		1	7	5		
	2		9	5		3		
9	7							
	1	6				2	5	
							3	7
		7		4	9		6	
		8	7	6		1		
6		2	5			9		

Puzzle 79   Easy

		5		3	8	4		9
8			5			1	7	
	4							8
				4	3			
1		3	8		7	5		4
			9	5				
3							1	
	1	4			9			6
6		7	3	1		9		

Puzzle 80   Easy

3	7			5	6		1	
					3	8		
8			1					7
	9		4	3		7		8
			9		8			
4		7		6	2		9	
1					5			9
		9	6					
	5		3	1			8	4

Sudoku

Puzzle 81   Easy

9				8			1	6
			9				3	
	8	1			4			
	4	2	8			1		5
	9		1		2		4	
1		7			3	6	8	
			6			7	5	
	1				8			
5	6			3				4

Puzzle 82   Easy

		8					2	
5					2	8	9	
	1							5
4		9	8	3		5		2
6			9		4			1
8		1		7	6	9		3
2							1	
	4	3	1					8
	8					4		

Sudoku

Puzzle 83 Easy

6	3		2	9				
				1	6		9	
		9					5	
5		6	1			2		
4	1		5		9		7	6
		2			4	5		1
	5					4		
	4		3	5				
				8	7		2	5

Puzzle 84 Easy

	9					7	6	
		4	2		3			
6			9	8				2
1		7	6				2	
3	2						5	4
	4				2	8		1
4				2	9			6
			8		1	3		
	1	8					9	

Sudoku

Puzzle 85   Easy

	9		8					7
	1			7	2	6		
			9	4	1			3
3				6			8	
		2	1		9	3		
	6			8				9
9			3	1	8			
		8	6	2			3	
2					4		6	

Puzzle 86   Easy

			6				7	
	1			3		9	2	
	8			2		5		6
		1			7			5
7	3		8		2		4	1
9			5			7		
3		2		8			5	
	7	8		5			6	
	9				6			

Puzzle 87   Easy

3				4				8
		6			9	7		
	1	7	3	2			4	
6			2	9	5			
		4				2		
			4	6	1			9
	6			1	2	3	8	
		3	9			6		
4				8				2

Puzzle 88   Easy

	9		2				5	
1		7	4					2
3		6	1		9	7		
	1	4						
8	3						2	5
						9	3	
		1	3		2	5		7
7					5	2		9
	4				7		1	

Sudoku

Puzzle 89 — Easy

5			9				6	2
	4	6		2			3	
2			6		4		1	
3						8	4	
	6						9	
	2	4						6
	7		3		9			4
	5			8		3	7	
4	8				1			5

Puzzle 90 — Easy

	1	4	5		7	3	2	
	2		3					9
		7		9				6
		1		2	9			
			6		3			
			4	7		9		
1				4		2		
6					5		9	
	4	3	9			2	6	1

Puzzle 91 — Easy

9				5				
2		7	8		4	5		
	8		7				9	3
				1	6		3	
7			9		8			5
	9		4	7				
4	2				7		5	
		1	2		9	3		7
				4				2

Puzzle 92 — Easy

3				4	6	2		1
				1			6	3
			3			8	4	7
		6					8	
5	1						7	4
	4					6		
6	5	4			1			
2	9			6				
1		7	5	8				6

Puzzle 93   Easy

7	9		5	2				
		8		7		3		
4		3			8	7		
	6			5		4		8
	8						3	
9		2		8			7	
		1	9			2		7
		9		4		5		
				1	7		4	9

Puzzle 94   Easy

6			8	7			9	1
				9		3		7
		5			1	4		
		3		6				5
		6	9		7	2		
7				5		8		
		7	1			9		
5		9		8				
1	4			2	9			3

Puzzle 95 Easy

	6			7		4		
			6	5	4			
4						6		1
		2	3	6		8		
6	7		2		1		5	3
		9		4	7	2		
7		5						9
			8	1	5			
		6		9			4	

Puzzle 96 Easy

	4		5	2	1		6	7
	2		8				9	
6							8	4
		6	2					
5			6		3			9
					5	8		
4	5							8
	7				8		4	
9	6		1	3	4		5	

Sudoku

Puzzle 97   Easy

	1		3	9				
	7	2	4				9	
					1	5		
	5	3		7			1	9
	8	7				3	5	
2	9			8		6	7	
		4	9					
	2				7	9	3	
				6	5		2	

Puzzle 98   Easy

	1				2			
5	8			7	4			
2		4				3	7	9
1				4	8			7
			7		1			
8			2	5				6
3	7	2				1		4
			4	3			6	2
			1				3	

53

Puzzle 99 Easy

		7		2	8			6
	6				7	3	4	2
					4	8	7	
		2	7					
	5	1				7	3	
				9	2			
	8	4	9					
7	2	6	5				8	
1			8	7		6		

Puzzle 100 Easy

		8	2				1	
			1	6	3	4		
1				7		3		2
7	8		6	3				
			7		8			
				1	5		8	6
4		3		8				5
	1	3	2	6				
	7				1	6		

Sudoku

Puzzle 101 — Easy

					7			3
5		7	3		1		4	
	8		5				2	1
		5					1	6
1	6						9	2
9	3					5		
2	5				3		6	
	1		6		5	2		4
3			1					

Puzzle 102 — Easy

					3	1		
7			8			2		
				4	7		6	
2		1	7	3		5	9	
9			4		5			6
	4	5		9	1	3		2
	5		3	8				
		7			2			1
		9	1					

55

Puzzle 103 Easy

		5			3	1		
	3		1	9				
		6	7					
	7	8	6	3		4		1
5		3				6		9
6		1		5	8	7	2	
					6	2		
				1	7		4	
		7	9			3		

Puzzle 104 Easy

			6			8	7	
					9	6		
9				8	2	1	5	
	1	3	2		5		8	
6								1
	7		1		8	5	6	
	3	6	9	4				8
		2	8					
	9	8			3			

Puzzle 105   Easy

				1	4		3	7
1	3				6	8		
			9			4	6	
			7	9		1		6
7								3
9		3		4	8			
	4	8			9			
		1	3				9	4
3	9		4	5				

Puzzle 106   Easy

3		1	6	7	2			
4		7		8				
	8			3				
7		3					5	
8	5	6				9	2	4
	1					8		7
			9				8	
			4			7		5
			2	5	3	4		1

Sudoku

Puzzle 107   Easy

3			2	8	1		9	
		8	7					4
	7				4		2	
	9	2	5					7
	8						5	
7					8	9	4	
	6		8				3	
2					7	5		
	5		1	3	2			9

Puzzle 108   Easy

1	4			3	5			6
						8		
			1		6	5	2	3
			4	6		1		
	3		5		1		6	
		1		2	9			
8	5	4	9		2			
		6						
3			6	5			1	8

Sudoku

8		1	9	2				
	4	2	7		5	8		
		6	8			9	2	
		4						
2	1						4	7
						1		
	6	9			4	3		
		5	3		1	2	7	
				6	7	4		8

						1		6
	6	1	3	8			4	
	5	7		6	1	8		
				7	8			2
		5				4		
6			1	4				
		6	7	3			2	1
	1			5	2	3	8	
5		2						

Puzzle 111   Easy

5	4	6			7		9	
	9			5	8			
			6	9				1
						7		8
7	6		9		3		4	5
4		5						
1				7	9			
			8	6			1	
	5		2			9	7	4

Puzzle 112   Easy

4	5	7		1				
	6	8	5			4		2
	2							1
9	1		4	3				
			7		1			
				2	9		6	4
5							4	
8		1			7	2	5	
				5		8	1	9

Sudoku

Puzzle 113 — Easy

		9					2	
					1	6	5	3
6		3	8		5	9	1	
			1	8				
	3		2		4		8	
				7	3			
	9	4	7			8	5		2
7	5	6	3					
	2					7		

Puzzle 114 — Easy

5	1	3	6			9		
7		2	5					
		6	1			2		7
			7			4		8
			9		2			
8		7			6			
2		9			1	7		
					5	1		9
		1			9	8	4	2

Puzzle 115   Easy

					9		8	
2	8			3				
5	4	7			8		3	
1			9	8				3
		8	2		3	5		
9				4	5			8
	2		8			3	7	5
				5			4	2
	3		4					

Puzzle 116   Easy

				7	1		9	
2		4	3					1
	7			6		5	3	
				1	6	2	8	
	1						7	
	8	6	5	2				
	3	7		9			2	
4					7	3		9
	2		1	3				

Sudoku

Puzzle 117 — Easy

			1			5		
4				7	2	1	9	
				9		3	2	
	5	4	9	2				
	3		4		6		5	
				3	5	2	4	
	4	6		5				
	2	9	3	1				5
		8			9			

Puzzle 118 — Easy

9		3			4	5		2
1	2	5	3				9	7
8			6					5
		4	9		1	2		
6					2			4
2	7				9	6	4	8
5		8	4			1		9

Puzzle 119   Easy

				7				9
		1	2	8	6			
	2			9			6	
		3	6			5		2
1	6	2				9	7	3
9		5			3	1		
	4			3			2	
			9	6	2	7		
2				5				

Puzzle 120   Easy

			6		4	9		
		2	7			8		1
4					1			7
				1	5	2		9
7		1				3		4
2		9	4	7				
9			1					8
1		5			7	4		
		4	9		3			

Sudoku

Puzzle 121 — Easy

5		7		9		8		
	4		2		1		9	5
			5			4		7
	8	1						
3		5				7		2
						5	8	
1		2			3			
9	5		8		2		7	
		8		5		2		3

Puzzle 122 — Easy

		7				9	2	
		2	5			3	8	
			2	3		1		
		1	7	5			3	
	9	5				4	1	
	6			4	1	2		
		6		1	3			
	3	4			2	8		
	2	8				7		

Puzzle 123   Easy

4			6					5
	6			7			9	1
8		7		9		4	2	
		1						
5	4		9		7		1	2
						5		
	2	5		1		7		4
1	8			5			6	
7					6			3

Puzzle 124   Easy

	5			6				3
8	4	3			5	2		
6								7
					3	9	7	8
	3		2		7		5	
1	8	7	6					
3								2
		5	3			1	4	9
9				2			3	

Sudoku

Puzzle 125 — Easy

	2	6						3
4				5				
7			8		3		2	6
9		2	3				8	
	3	4				7	5	
	7				5	6		9
2	4		7		9			8
				3				7
3						2	9	

Puzzle 126 — Easy

	5		8		3			7
7	4				2	6		
8		2		7				3
					6	8		
2			9		8			5
		8	2					
3				8		2		1
		7	1				3	9
1			3		5		8	

67

Puzzle 127   Easy

3				6	5	2	7	
			1				6	
		1		4	3		9	8
	1				6			
4	2						3	6
			3				2	
1	3		5	8		6		
	8				4			
	5	4	2	1				3

Puzzle 128   Easy

					6	1	8	
				5				
	9			2		6	4	5
1		4	7		3	2		
	2		5		4		7	
		9	8		2	4		1
5	1	3		4			9	
				8				
	4	8	6					

Sudoku

Puzzle 129 — Easy

9		7		3				
5					8	3		2
3	8		7	6				
				4		1		
4	5	1				7	2	9
	7		2					
			2	7			3	8
1		9	8					7
				4		1		5

Puzzle 130 — Easy

	4						9	1
3	8	9			6			5
		6	9		5			4
	5	7			9			
		3				8		
			3			9	5	
8			4		3	2		
9			6			4	1	8
2	6						3	

Puzzle 131   Easy

3			2			1		
	4				1		3	6
	9							2
7	5		4		6		1	
		6	7		5	3		
	1		3		8		6	7
6							4	
5	7		6				8	
		8			9			5

Puzzle 132   Easy

		7			1	9		3
			7		3			
5	3						1	
	6	3	9	7			2	1
2								9
7	9			5	6	8	3	
	2						8	5
			8		5			
3		5	4			1		

Sudoku

Puzzle 133   Easy

1			3				6	
		8	7	6	9		3	
3								9
6				5	3	8		2
	9						5	
8		7	1	4				3
7								5
	8		5	3	1	9		
	3				7			6

Puzzle 134   Easy

							6	2
1	8		2			5		
6			5	3	7			
		6		5	1	4		
8	7						3	5
		1	3	7		6		
			9	6	3			7
		3			5		8	4
7	9							

Puzzle 135   Easy

						6		8
2	9	7		8		4		
	8			1	7			5
	6		3	7	9			1
7			2	6	5		9	
8			7	2			6	
		6		5		1	3	2
1		2						

Puzzle 136   Easy

6				3				
			7	8		9	2	1
					5			
8	7	1	6		3			2
	6		2		8		1	
2			9		4	6	7	8
			5					
1	4	5		6	7			
				2				6

Sudoku

					1	8	2	
	4							
8		1		5				4
5	1	6	8	7		9		
2			6		5			8
		8		2	9	6	5	7
9				8		7		6
							8	
	8	2	7					

3	5		1	4	2			
7		1	6	3	5			
6								
2	8		4					
		6	9		3	7		
					1		2	9
								1
			5	1	6	3		4
			3	8	4		7	2

Puzzle 139   Easy

						1		
	4	2	1		6	8		5
1					2		3	
		4	6				1	8
	5		7		1		2	
2	9				8	6		
	1		8					3
4		3	2		9	7	8	
		8						

Puzzle 140   Easy

3		9						5
			1					
5	8	7	2	9		4		
	6			3		8		4
	5		8		6		2	
4		8		1			7	
		4		2	9	1	5	3
					1			
1						6		2

Puzzle 141 — Easy

				9		7	6	
				4			2	
	8					1	4	9
5					1	9	8	
8		9	5		4	6		7
	6	1	8					4
6	5	2					7	
	7			1				
	4	8		5				

Puzzle 142 — Easy

			5			3		
			6		3	9		8
3	6	1			2			
6				3				2
2		3	1		8	7		4
7				2				6
			8			6	7	9
9		6	2		1			
		7			6			

Puzzle 143   Easy

7		9			1			
		2	4			7		1
			8	7		5		
3				2	9	1		6
6								2
2		1	6	5				7
		3		6	5			
4		7		9		2		
			7			3		9

Puzzle 144   Easy

	8	9			5			2
2				1				
	1		9	2	3			
				2		6	7	5
		4	9		7	8		
1	7	6		8				
		1	4	7			9	
				5				7
9			2			5	4	

Puzzle 145 Easy

				7		9	8	
8	4			5		1		
		9					5	7
	7	3			2			9
6			1		7			5
5			3			2	7	
9	8					7		
		4		6			2	1
	2	6		1				

Puzzle 146 Easy

3					8	5	2	
5		4		6				
		2	1				4	8
					2	1		4
	2		4			5		6
4		8	7					
8	4				1	6		
				8		7		3
	3	7	6					5

Puzzle 147   Easy

1	2		9			5		
8			1					
	7	9			4	3		
5	1		6		2	4	9	
	3	4	7		5		2	6
		6	2			7	5	
				1				3
		1			7		6	4

Puzzle 148   Easy

9	2						5	7
	8		2		6			
4				5			9	2
				7	3			6
	7		1		9		2	
5			6	2				
2	5			3				4
			7		5		1	
1	4						7	3

Sudoku

Puzzle 149 — Easy

1		9	4		8		6	
2	8	4				9		
			1					
3				6	5			
8	4		5		9		1	3
		5	2					6
				1				
		1				8	3	7
	6		7		5	1		9

Puzzle 150 — Easy

7	9				5	3		
5	3	4			1		8	
		8		4				
		3	5	1				
1			7		2			9
				8	6	7		
				5		8		
	5		1			4	3	2
		9	4				7	5

Puzzle 151 Easy

7	2	4		1				6
		5			2	4		
6	9		4					
				9		6		
4	7	6				8	3	9
	1		3					
				4			2	7
		7	1			6		
5				2		1	4	3

Puzzle 152 Easy

6		9	8		5	3		4
	8	3						
7				9				
3			1	4				
4		8	5		6	9		1
				8	9			3
				5				7
						2	4	
5		6	4		7	1		8

Sudoku

Puzzle 153 — Easy

7			8		4		6	3
	5			7		2	8	
3			2		9			
	4		7				5	
5								4
	3				2		1	
			4		5			8
	6	4		8			3	
8	7		6		3			2

Puzzle 154 — Easy

2			3		9	1	6	7
	7						4	2
						3		
5		1			4		3	
	9		8		3		1	
	3		5			2		6
		7						
9	8						7	
6	2	4	9		7			3

Puzzle 155 — Easy

				4				6
	4		9	1			5	2
			2			7		
2			6	5		1		
9	1		3		2		4	5
		4		9	1			7
		1			8			
6	8			3	9		2	
3				2				

Puzzle 156 — Easy

		8	4					
	3	1	8		5		2	
	7			2	6			
3						6	4	7
4		5				2		3
7	1	6						5
			9	1			7	
	4		6		7	8	5	
					4	1		

Sudoku

1		6	2				7	
	2				8		1	5
4	9				1			
	7	1		9				
3			6		7			9
			8		1	3		
			1				5	8
5	4		8				6	
	1				6	4		3

		2		3		1		
		3	5	8	2		7	
6								2
7	6			1	8			5
5								7
3			7	4			6	8
2								1
	5		3	2	4	6		
		6		7		5		

Puzzle 159 Easy

			6		1		4	8
					8			1
			5	3		6	2	7
	1					2		6
7			9		6			4
4		8					1	
5	2	4		6	3			
6			4					
8	3		1		9			

Puzzle 160 Easy

7			3		8		4	
				6				8
	6		5			2		
6	8	9	2			1		4
1								6
2		4			1	8	9	7
		3			6		8	
9				3				
	4		7		2			3

Sudoku

	8			3				
5		6	2			3	8	9
			6	5		4		
2		7			3		5	
	9						3	
	3		5			7		2
		4		7	5			
7	5	1			2	8		6
				6			7	

			9				2	1
6		1		8		5		
	3	2				8		
	1	6	7				4	3
	4						7	
3	2				5	9	6	
		3				4	1	
		9		6		3		2
4	6				1			

Puzzle 163 Easy

8	1			2		6		
	6				8			3
		3						2
3					2		4	5
	2	4	7		3	8	9	
9	5		8					6
7						3		
2			4				6	
		8		3			2	7

Puzzle 164 Easy

5				2		4		
4					6	8		
	8	6				5	7	
			2	8			1	
7	3		1		5		8	2
	2			6	9			
	6	7				2	9	
		4	6					7
		2		7				8

Sudoku

Moderate

		4			3		8
					6		2
9	3	7	8				
			2		7		
1			9	7	8		3
		2			4		
				5	8	2	4
4		8					
6		3			1		

Puzzle 166 Moderate

	6		4	1				
4		7					5	
3		8		5	6			
5		4		3				
		2				9		
				2		5		7
			8	6		3		9
	8					4		5
				4	7		8	

87

Sudoku

Puzzle 167 Moderate

	8					7	5	
				3	7			
					9	4		2
8	9							
6			8		2			9
							2	1
3		6	2					
			3	4				
	5	4					6	

Puzzle 168 Moderate

	9	4			5			
		6	4					9
							1	
7	5				3		6	
6			2		1			5
	3		6				9	1
	6							
1					4	2		
			8			1	3	

Sudoku

Puzzle 169 — Moderate

7				6	4			8
							9	
2		4	5	7				
		3		8	7			1
5			6	1		2		
				5	2	4		9
	4							
1			3	4				2

Puzzle 170 — Moderate

	6			7		8		
							3	1
9			1	3	8			
					1		8	6
7		6				3		9
5	1		9					
			5	4	7			3
3	4							
		5		1			2	

Puzzle 171 Moderate

5						8		
8			5	6			4	
	3							1
	8							2
2		6		1		7		4
4							9	
7							1	
	1			2	9			3
		5						6

Puzzle 172 Moderate

				8	3			
3			1				5	2
			4				1	3
9	4				6			7
				4				
8			7				3	9
6	9				2			
7	2				4			5
			9	1				

Sudoku

Puzzle 173   Moderate

						3		
5			9			1		2
6	1	2						8
				4				3
		3	7	1	8	6		
9				3				
7						5	6	4
3		6			7			9
		1						

Puzzle 174   Moderate

3			1	7	6			
			9	8				
	8			4		9		
5		7					9	
9	3						1	5
	1					7		3
		2		9			8	
				2	7			
			6	3	5			2

Puzzle 175 Moderate

			3			4		
					2		7	3
3				4			8	2
							6	
8		6	5	2	3	7		9
	9							
5	2			8				4
6	7		9					
		3			1			

Puzzle 176 Moderate

		1						6
			6			7		8
6				7	8			
9			5			8	2	
5								1
	4	3			6			7
			2	8				4
3		9			1			
4						3		

Sudoku

Puzzle 177 — Moderate

		6						2
			7			6		
2				8	6			4
7					8	5		
	2	9			7	4		
	9	5						8
3			1	9				5
	1				2			
4						8		

Puzzle 178 — Moderate

					9	3	5	8
			3		6		1	
			1				2	7
2		1				8		
	4						7	
		5				1		3
5	8				1			
	1		4		3			
4	3	6	8					

Puzzle 179 Moderate

			5		1	8		
	2						7	
		6		3				
9						2		
6		7	2	4	8	9		3
		3						6
				9		1		
	7						5	
		9	8		4			

Puzzle 180 Moderate

	6							8
	3						4	
			9	6	7			
		4		1				9
3			7		8			1
8				3		2		
			8	2	1			
	1						2	
5							3	

Sudoku

Puzzle 181 — Moderate

	5	7	4					
		3	5	7	8		6	
		5				7		2
1				6				9
8		9				4		
	1		7	3	5	9		
					2	1	7	

Puzzle 182 — Moderate

	9			6				7
					1	6	4	
4				8		9		
7							9	
		5	3	2	7	4		
	8							5
		9		7				3
	1	7	5					
3				4			6	

Sudoku

Puzzle 183 Moderate

4				5				
3		7					4	6
		2				5		
	2		5	1				
1			8		4			3
				7	6		2	
		9				2		
5	6					4		8
				4				7

Puzzle 184 Moderate

	8					6		7
					1		2	
			6			4	3	
		4	8					
3	1	5				7	8	6
					5	9		
	5	7			4			
	6		9					
2		1					6	

Sudoku

Puzzle 185   Moderate

	2		8					
				9	4		1	5
	9			3		7		
9						6	7	
	5	2				4	3	
	7	8						9
		9		1			2	
3	1		4	6				
					5		6	

Puzzle 186   Moderate

			7					5
	6					1	3	
3					8			
8		4			2	7		
	7		1		3		4	
		3	4			8		9
			2					4
	2	9					6	
5					1			

Sudoku

Puzzle 187 — Moderate

8					1	2		3
	1		4		7			
								1
7			1	4	5	6		
		5	3	9	6			2
5								
			6		3		9	
4		1	8					5

Puzzle 188 — Moderate

1				3	4			
	5	8	1					
				7				8
	7					2	3	
		4		2		9		
	8	6					7	
4				8				
					3	1	4	
			6	4				3

Sudoku

Puzzle 189   Moderate

	9		5	3				2
1		8					3	
				8	1			9
				4	7			1
	1						9	
8			1	9				
7			4	5				
	2					9		3
9				7	2		8	

Puzzle 190   Moderate

8		7			6	9		
			7					1
			2		5		4	
7		9						
	2	5		4		1	7	
						2		4
	7		6		4			
1					3			
		4	9			6		2

Puzzle 191 Moderate

5		2						
				9	1		6	2
		7	2					
8	9				2			
		5	4		8	2		
			7				1	5
					7	1		
2	4		8	1				
						3		8

Puzzle 192 Moderate

		8	1					
6			3					
	2	1		8	5			
3		5		9				7
	4		5		2		9	
2				3		6		5
			4	6		7	5	
					3			9
					7	8		

Sudoku

	5		9					1
	3		7		6			
1		4						
7		5		9		8		
		1		8		4		3
						5		7
		6		3		9		
4					8		3	

		9			1	7		
						2		8
3	2				5			1
	8		2				1	
9		5				4		2
	1				9		7	
4			1				9	5
8		6						
		1	5			6		

Puzzle 195   Moderate

1				5	8			
3		4						6
		7					4	
	3			8	2		6	
8			5		4			2
	4		1	6			8	
	5				9			
6						3		5
			6	2				4

Puzzle 196   Moderate

			6			8		2
	8		2		5		7	
6							5	
7	3				2			
			5		4			
			9				3	4
	5							1
	6		4		3		2	
1		2			6			

Sudoku

Puzzle 197   Moderate

		6						2
	9			6		7		
			2	7			8	
3		4				9	6	
	5						1	
	2	1				3		7
	6			4	8			
		2		3			7	
7						4		

Puzzle 198   Moderate

				4		6		
	3				6	2	1	
8					9			
4			9				6	
		5		2		8		
	2				7			9
			1					4
	7	9	8				5	
		1		6				

Sudoku

Puzzle 199 Moderate

6						1		
	1	2			3			9
		5	2		1			
	6		3	2	4			5
5			1	8	9		4	
			7		2	8		
8			5			7	1	
		1						4

Puzzle 200 Moderate

		6			5		8	
7		8				2		
			3				7	
	8			5	3	6		
				1				
		9	2	6			4	
	6				1			
		4				1		7
	2		6			9		

Puzzle 201 — Moderate

	6		2				3	
				9				8
		7	8		3			4
		2				1	4	
		9		7		3		
	8	6				5		
6			3		1	2		
8				2				
	2				6		7	

Puzzle 202 — Moderate

5		2		8				6
			6					3
7	1				3			8
9		3	5					
	4						7	
					9	4		2
6			9				3	4
3					6			
4				3		8		7

Sudoku

Puzzle 203 — Moderate

		1					7	6
		4	6	3		2		
2					1		8	
4			1				6	2
1	5				9			4
	1		8					5
		5		1	7	3		
8	9					6		

Puzzle 204 — Moderate

8	3	9		2				
5					7			
	2	1			3		4	
			1			3		
1	8						7	5
		3			5			
	5		4			8	3	
			5					6
				9		5	1	4

Sudoku

Puzzle 205 — Moderate

		5	8	7				1
							9	4
	3	1		5	2			
		6					5	
5			2		3			6
	7					8		
			5	2		9	8	
9	2							
8				1	9	4		

Puzzle 206 — Moderate

7	9					3		5
			2			7		
			6	3				
	3		8					6
2			4		6			9
8					3		2	
				6	1			
		7			8			
3		9					4	1

Sudoku

Puzzle 207 Moderate

4	7		5		1			
		2					6	
		9				4		
			1		2	5		9
			4		8			
5		1	3		7			
		8				1		
	3					2		
			2		6		7	5

Puzzle 208 Moderate

4			8	5		2		
							3	
					4	9		5
	1					7	2	
		5	2	6	9	4		
	2	4					8	
5		1	7					
	6							
		3		2	6			7

108

Sudoku

Puzzle 209 — Moderate

	1	9	5		4	2		
	3	2	7			1		9
4								
		3	8					
7								8
			9	7				
								2
6		4			1	9	3	
		7	6		9	4	8	

Puzzle 210 — Moderate

			4		5	2		
	8				3			5
						8	6	
	6	4	8					2
	1			2			4	
8					4	6	9	
	4	3						
6			9				2	
		9	3		7			

109

Puzzle 211 — Moderate

	1			7	4			
6		4					9	8
		8						
					9		8	
3		2		6		9		5
	7		2					
						3		
4	5					8		7
			5	3			6	

Puzzle 212 — Moderate

		5					4	
	3				8			7
		8		3				
3	1		9	5		4		
9								5
		7		6	4		1	3
				9		5		
5			2				3	
	7					8		

Sudoku

Puzzle 213 — Moderate

	8	1	5				6	7
				4	9			8
								1
		6		5	7			3
			3		9			
5			4	6		1		
1								
3		2	7					
4	5				2	3	1	

Puzzle 214 — Moderate

5					1			3
	9				4			8
1			9			2		
	5				3			
	3			7			9	
			2				6	
	1			3				4
3			8				1	
6			9					2

Puzzle 215 Moderate

	7		1					
	2				7	3		
		3		6			8	
				5		8	3	7
9								1
4	5	8		3				
	8			2		1		
		5	3				2	
					6		9	

Puzzle 216 Moderate

	8					4		
3						6		
	1		2			7		5
8					9	1		
	3		6		4		5	
		2	7					3
7		3			5		4	
		8						6
		9					1	

Sudoku

Puzzle 217 — Moderate

		8			7	3		
	9				8	7		
	5	3		2				
			9			4		
4	6						7	1
		7			6			
				1		6	4	
		4	5				2	
		1	8			9		

Puzzle 218 — Moderate

7					5			
4				8				3
		2		3		4		8
	9							
5		6	8		1	2		7
							8	
6		8		4		1		
9				7				6
			6					2

Sudoku

Puzzle 219 — Moderate

			9			7	1	
6				3	7			
	5				1			
1						4		
3	4		7		8		2	9
		2						6
			2				7	
			5	7				4
	2	3			4			

Puzzle 220 — Moderate

					4			1
	7			1				2
4			6		2	7		
		2	1			8		6
			4		3			
5		7			6	1		
		4	3		1			7
3				7			5	
7			8					

Sudoku

Puzzle 221   Moderate

5		2	3				6	
6	8		9					
						8		5
		8	2	7		6		
9								2
		1		3	9	5		
7		9						
					4		3	6
	6				3	2		1

Puzzle 222   Moderate

3		2	9		4	1		
	7	5	8					9
			8	2		6	1	
2	8		5	3				
8					1	5	3	
		4	7		5	8		2

Puzzle 223 Moderate

				6		3	1	5
			2	5	3	7	9	
				2	4			8
		9		1		6		
2			9	3				
	6	8	4	9	5			
3	9	5		8				

Puzzle 224 Moderate

1				6			9	
		8	3					
9			1		8		5	
4	8		7					
	7			4			3	
					6		8	7
	4		2		5			1
					4	5		
	2			3				8

Sudoku

Puzzle 225 — Moderate

						3		
2				6	8		4	7
1					4		9	
			3				6	1
			8	4	6			
5	6				1			
	8		9					3
7	4		6	1				5
		2						

Puzzle 226 — Moderate

3			9	7				2
			8				7	
			4			1		6
	7					5	9	
		4	7		8	6		
	5	3					2	
7		8		2				
	6				3			
1			9	7				8

Sudoku

Puzzle 227　　Moderate

	8	7			4			
		3			6			
	5	9	1	8		7		
8								1
		6		9		5		
1								2
		2		5	8	1	3	
			7			2		
			6			9	8	

Puzzle 228　　Moderate

	1			5			3	
		9			7			
	5				8	9	1	
6								5
3	8						9	4
4								2
	2	3	7				5	
			3			7		
	4			1			8	

Sudoku

Puzzle 229 — Moderate

5			2		9		6	7
7							9	
							1	
			8		6		7	
8				4				5
	7		3		5			
	1							
	5							2
2	8		5		7			3

Puzzle 230 — Moderate

9			5	7				
		4	8		3			
5								8
4	2	8				6		
	5						3	
		1				2	8	9
2								5
			1		4	7		
				9	7			3

Puzzle 231 Moderate

					6	4		
	7	9						
2			8		4	5		
6		2		5				
5				8				6
				3		1		5
		7	1		5			9
						8	5	
		1	2					

Puzzle 232 Moderate

	8			6				
5		6		2				4
		7		1		6		2
	9		7		1			
7								8
			4		2		6	
1		3		9		2		
4				7		5		1
				4			8	

Sudoku

Puzzle 233 — Moderate

					9	1		
1					7		2	
	8	3		4	6			
		2						3
8	4			9			7	5
3						4		
			7	1		8	6	
	1		6					2
		7	9					

Puzzle 234 — Moderate

5				1	8			4
	8			7				
	9		2		5			
		6			1		5	
		4				2		
	5		6			9		
			1		4		7	
				5			4	
6			8	3				5

Sudoku

Puzzle 235 — Moderate

3	1	7			8			
	5				3			
8		6	5		2		1	
1		9						
6								1
						7		5
	9		8		5	3		4
			3				8	
			4			1	5	9

Puzzle 236 — Moderate

		5		8	6			
3				5			6	
4			3		7	1		
							2	3
		7		1		9		
9	2							
		6	8		4			1
	8			6				9
		2	7		6			

Sudoku

Puzzle 237 Moderate

			7			1		
		7					8	2
	5		2			7		
	6			5				8
	1			3			5	
4				6			9	
		1			8		7	
5	9					2		
		6			1			

Puzzle 238 Moderate

1			4	9				
2		3				4		
5							1	
		9	6	3	8			
7				2				8
			9	1	7	5		
	8							5
		7				1		9
				4	6			2

123

Puzzle 239 Moderate

3		9	1	6				5
		1		2		7		
					9		3	
				5				6
5		2				4		3
4				9				
	8		2					
		4		1		3		
6				4	5	9		7

Puzzle 240 Moderate

				1	3			
3		4	2					
	6					7	3	
6		9	5				2	
	1		6		2		5	
	4				7	6		9
	9	6					8	
					9	2		4
			8	2				

Sudoku

Puzzle 241 — Moderate

4				6		1		2
	9		7		2	4		
2					5		3	
		6	8					
	8						2	
					7	5		
	5		3					9
		2	5		6		4	
6		3		7				5

Puzzle 242 — Moderate

3				4		9	2	
6					3		4	
9			6				5	3
			3					
4			5		1			2
					6			
5	3				9			7
	9		7					8
	6	7		1				4

125

Puzzle 243 Moderate

	5	7				1	3	
4	3					8		
	1				4			
			7	1				6
				4				
6				2	5			
			9				5	
		4					6	7
	7	8				2	9	

Puzzle 244 Moderate

	2		3					
			6	7			3	
3				1		5		2
		8		4		7		
4	7						2	9
		9		2		1		
9		3		8				1
	1			3	6			
				9		4		

Sudoku

7			4	3	6			
	6		9					
		3						5
3		9		8				7
		7		6		1		
1				9		5		8
5						8		
					7		9	
			8	1	3			4

			5	2			8	
5			8	4		7		
		9				5		1
2	6			1		3		
		7		3			9	8
3		5				6		
		2		5	4			9
	9			7	2			

Puzzle 247   Moderate

8				5			7	
	2					1		
	9		8		3		5	
		5	9				1	
		9		8		7		
	6				4	5		
	8		3		7		4	
		4					3	
	1			6				7

Puzzle 248   Moderate

	6			5		8		
	2		6		1			9
	7		2			6		
9						5	2	
	5	1						7
		6			2		3	
3			9		7		6	
		2		8			4	

128

Sudoku

Puzzle 249 — Moderate

			7					3
3	9					1	7	
						8	9	
			6		1			2
	1		2	5	8		6	
5			9		3			
	8	7						
	3	9					1	4
4					7			

Puzzle 250 — Moderate

						9	5	
7				8	9			3
			4	2		7		
		9			2			
		2	9		3	5		
			7			4		
		3		6	1			
5			2	7				6
	4	7						

Puzzle 251 Moderate

		7		6			1	
3					2			7
	5		4					8
		9					7	
			5	3	8			
	2					3		
8					4		2	
1			7					4
	4			9		7		

Puzzle 252 Moderate

		1					6	
7					5	9		
	3					7		4
		7	2				8	9
3			7		6			2
2	4				8	6		
8		2					4	
		4	6					1
	9					2		

Sudoku

	4		9					
					8	4		
		3		4			9	5
			5	8			4	7
5				9				6
4	9			1	3			
1	3			5		7		
		6	4					
					6		5	

	4	2						8
			3			7		
1				8	4	6		
9			4			2	3	
			6		3			
	3	6			7			9
		3	1	4				2
		8			9			
2						1	6	

Puzzle 255   Moderate

				2	5			
		6	1			2		
7				3				
	7						3	2
8			5	4	6			7
4	1						8	
				8				3
		3			1	9		
			9	5				

Puzzle 256   Moderate

	5			6			7	
3								
			1	9		2		
5	9		6					3
	2	3				6	9	
4					1		2	5
		1		8	4			
								4
	8			1			6	

Sudoku

Puzzle 257 — Moderate

						2		
5	1		9	2	3			
	7							
	5	4	3					2
6			1		4			3
8					2	9	4	
							1	
			7	3	1		2	6
		8						

Puzzle 258 — Moderate

			6			2		3
			3		1	8	4	
	7	3	2					
3	9					4		
	4						7	
		2					6	9
					2	5	8	
	5	8	1		3			
4		7			5			

Puzzle 259 Moderate

		1	9	7			6	
					6	2		
6	2				8		4	
9		3						
	6			8			7	
						1		6
	1		8				5	2
		8	4					
	7			2	9	8		

Puzzle 260 Moderate

3							1	5
		7	9					
6	4		8					9
7			1		9	3		8
9		1	6		8			4
1					6		8	3
					4	2		
4	6							1

Sudoku

	1		7		8			
	9			6				4
	5				1		8	6
			1	2				
3			6		4			1
				3	7			
5	3		4				9	
1				8			2	
			3		6		1	

7		9						
	8		2			4		
	2			5	1		9	
9		2		1			4	
5								8
	7			4		2		9
	1		8	2			6	
		6			4		8	
						9		1

Puzzle 263 Moderate

		9	5	8		2		
	1				2			
				6		4		
	2		9					3
7								6
5					6		9	
		5		4				
			1				3	
		3		7	8	1		

Puzzle 264 Moderate

5	7	1						4
	8		4					5
				8				6
	4				2	1		
			3	4	8			
		5	9				3	
1				2				
4					9		2	
9						5	7	1

Puzzle 265 Moderate

	3	5	9				6	
		4	8					3
		6				8		
5	7		1		9			
				3				
			2		5		9	8
		1				4		
6					4	5		
	4				2	1	3	

Puzzle 266 Moderate

			3	4	2			
1								9
	8		1					
	9				3		6	5
5		2		1		9		3
7	3		6				4	
					4		3	
2								7
			8	3	1			

Puzzle 267 — Moderate

	4	2			8	9		
				4				2
3					2	8		
9			6				8	4
8	6				3			5
		4	9					8
7				3				
		1	7			6	3	

Puzzle 268 — Moderate

				3			2	7
		3	7					4
		4			9	1	8	
4								
		8	3	6	1	7		
								9
	3	6	1			4		
8					5	3		
1	4			2				

Sudoku

Puzzle 269 — Moderate

7				2	5	3		
			6				9	
		5			1		7	
	1				6			
8								9
			4				6	
	5		9			2		
	3				8			
		9	7	4				3

Puzzle 270 — Moderate

			9		8			
		6				3	9	
	8	7	3			5		1
					6	7		
1				2				6
		8	7					
7		9			5	1	3	
	4	5				9		
			2		7			

Puzzle 271 Moderate

			7	9	4			
		5						4
3				2			8	
		2			7		3	8
	3						7	
8	7		2			4		
	5			3				9
1						2		
			1	5	6			

Puzzle 272 Moderate

		3	2		7		6	
2				3				7
							3	4
				6				1
	4	2				5	9	
9				8				
3	2							
5				7				9
	9		5			6	1	

Sudoku

Puzzle 273 — Moderate

			3					
	7	8	5		1		9	
		2			6		5	
6						4		
	3	9				7	8	
		4						1
	6		8			9		
	1		7		3	8	4	
				5				

Puzzle 274 — Moderate

			2		7	6	8	
					3			5
		2					4	3
			8		5	9	3	
	8						6	
	9	1	3		2			
1	7					4		
9			5					
	2	6	7		9			

Puzzle 275   Moderate

4		7			1		6	9
9		8		6				5
		1						
				3		9		2
			7		2			
5		2		9				
						5		
8				4		6		1
3	7		9			8		4

Puzzle 276   Moderate

	4			5	2			
			7	6			9	
5	9		1					
1						9		2
6		9				7		4
4		3						1
					1		5	3
	1			8	5			
			4	7			1	

Puzzle 277 Moderate

	1			4				
2			6			4		
8	6			2				
		3	9					
5	4			3			6	1
					6	3		
				6			7	2
		7			2			8
				8			3	

Puzzle 278 Moderate

							9	
5	6				2	8	7	
			3		4		2	
			4		5	1		
	9						3	
		1	7		6			
	5		6		3			
	7	2	8				5	3
	1							

143

Sudoku

Puzzle 279 — Moderate

8				6				
4		2			7	6	8	
	6					7		
					1	5		
2			3	9	5			1
		4	7					
		1					7	
	4	9	1			3		6
				3				4

Puzzle 280 — Moderate

4			8	3				2
		2			1			9
		7	9	5			3	
1	3		4					
					3		1	6
	6			8	5	7		
8			7			9		
7				9	6			5

144

Sudoku

Puzzle 281 Moderate

	2						1	
			8	2	9			6
4			1	5				
	6	8			4	3		
	5						6	
		3	6			7	9	
				6	5			7
5			2	7	3			
	3						5	

Puzzle 282 Moderate

			7				9	8
1				6		4		
	2				4	5		
		7	5	1			4	3
4	5			7	9	8		
		5	4				7	
		3		5				9
7	1				6			

Puzzle 283 Moderate

	3			9			8	
8		2				1		
5			7			9		
1			5	8				
			4	7				2
		7		3				9
		3				6		4
	6			7			3	

Puzzle 284 Moderate

8		7						
		2	6					1
	3				5			
7				1			8	
	8	5		3		7	6	
	4			2				9
			2				9	
5					4	8		
						6		4

Sudoku

	4				7		5	1
2			8					
			3	6	5	2		
		3						5
7			5		8			9
8						3		
		8	7	9	2			
					3			2
9	7		6				3	

			5			8	6	9
				8				5
						2	4	
4		6		7			2	
1			2		5			4
	9			6		3		7
	5	7						
2			3					
6	4	3			9			

Puzzle 287 Moderate

	5	4	6	1				
		8			2			
			8				1	6
		7	5				4	8
	8						6	
5	4				6	7		
8	7				5			
			7			4		
				9	3	5	8	

Puzzle 288 Moderate

	7		1					
					4	9		7
4					3	8		
9	8							
	3		7		5		8	
							5	2
		9	4					6
5		1	3					
					2		7	

Sudoku

Puzzle 289 — Moderate

		1					2	5
7			3					8
			2					
	7			3		1	6	
1			9		4			2
	3	5		1			7	
					6			
4					8			6
8	2					9		

Puzzle 290 — Moderate

		6				5		7
8			5	1		6		
			2					
4				3				
	7	9	4		8	1	6	
				6				9
					3			
		8		2	9			6
1		2				4		

Sudoku

Puzzle 291 — Moderate

		2		9	8			3
6					3		9	
		3				8		
8		7						
4			7	5	6			8
						1		6
		8				6		
	2		1					9
7			5	8		4		

Puzzle 292 — Moderate

					8	1	4	
	9	3	7					8
3	1		5	6				7
2								9
4				1	2		3	5
9					5	3	8	
	6	7	3					

Sudoku

Puzzle 293 Moderate

		8		5				
	7							9
4	2				8			
	4	3	7					
7			2	1	9			3
					3	6	8	
			1				3	5
2							7	
				3		1		

Puzzle 294 Moderate

					9	2	1	
				5	6	7		3
	9					5		
3			8	1		4		
		7		4	5			1
		6					3	
8		5	1	7				
	7	1	2					

151

Sudoku

Puzzle 295 — Moderate

		7	2		6	9	5	
	2			1	7			
4					9	1		
		8					4	
		1		3				
	9					6		
		9	6					5
			3	2			9	
	8	6	9		1	3		

Puzzle 296 — Moderate

						8		3
	3		2				9	
	8							4
		3	8		6			9
		7	1		9	3		
9			5		7	6		
3							5	
	2				3		4	
7		1						

Sudoku

Puzzle 297 — Moderate

3				8		9		5
	6				7	8	1	
	1		2	3			5	8
		3				6		
8	5			6	1		4	
	9	1	8				3	
4		5		2				9

Puzzle 298 — Moderate

	2				5	8	3	
1								
			9	4	1			
	9			1				6
	8	1				2	9	
6				4			1	
		2	9	7				
								1
	4	3	6				2	

Sudoku

Puzzle 299 — Moderate

	9			6		4		
				1			7	3
		2	5				6	
5			8			6	4	
	7	4			3			9
	6				1	7		
3	1			4				
		8		2			3	

Puzzle 300 — Moderate

				9		2	4	3
	8				2			
3			4				8	1
							2	6
			3		5			
6	1							
5	2				1			7
			5				9	
9	4	3		8				

154

Sudoku

3	5				8		4	
	8			2				
9		4	7					
					1		3	7
			6	7	2			
6	4		8					
					7	3		9
				9			5	
	3		4				7	6

Puzzle 302   Moderate

	7			1		4		
			6			3	5	
6		5						9
2					4	6		
5			7		9			4
		4	8					7
7						2		6
	5	9				3		
		2		7			4	

Puzzle 303 Moderate

						5		
1	3	7						2
	9				2		4	
		2		7			1	5
				1				
4	5			9		7		
	7		4				2	
3						1	8	7
		8						

Puzzle 304 Moderate

			4		6		9	
2			5			8		
	6	9	1				2	
		8	3			6		
4								5
		3			4	1		
	9				1	3	5	
		5			9			1
	3		6		7			

Puzzle 305 Moderate

	4	1		7				8
6								7
			3		8	2		
		7		5	6			1
3			4	1		5		
		6	8		4			
7								5
8				9		4	2	

Puzzle 306 Moderate

					4			
			3	9		2		
4	3	8			5			
9			5		6		1	8
	7						4	
6	1		8		7			2
			1			4	2	6
		9		5	2			
			4					

Sudoku

Puzzle 307 Moderate

		5	7			2		
		4		3			9	5
2			5					
		1		8			4	
8			4		6			3
	5			2		9		
					8			9
9	1			4		8		
		8			1	7		

Puzzle 308 Moderate

		7		5	4			
		1		3	2			4
	5	3	7					
		2		6		8		7
1		8		2		6		
					5	3	4	
8			2	4		1		
			6	1		5		

Puzzle 309 Moderate

			3		8			
8	3			1			7	
	4			6		8		
		5			3	2		
2				7				5
		4	1			9		
		2		5			3	
	5			3			4	6
			8		7			

Puzzle 310 Moderate

6	1						7	
					2		6	
	7	2		6		9	1	
		4		9	7			
		9				8		
			3	4		5		
	9	7		1		6	3	
	3		7					
	8						5	1

Puzzle 311   Moderate

6			4				5	
		9			2			
	4		6			1		
		1			4			3
8		4		7		9		5
9			3			7		
		8			6		1	
			7			6		
	9				3			2

Puzzle 312   Moderate

1								
			5	7				6
	5	3	6				7	
4			2	1		8		
		8				7		
		2		4	7			5
	3				8	5	9	
5				6	9			
								1

Puzzle 313 Moderate

7					6		5	
	5			4				
		2			1	8	9	
1					7			
	8	9	4		3	2	1	
			8					5
	9	4	3			1		
				2			3	
	3		1					9

Puzzle 314 Moderate

2					6	1		
						4	6	
			9		1	8		3
3			1		2			5
	1						2	
5			8		3			1
9		5	7		8			
	8	3						
		6	5					8

Puzzle 315 Moderate

	1	6		8				4
2		5						
			9	2			5	
	3					4	7	5
8	6	7					9	
	9			3	2			
						3		6
3				5		7	2	

Puzzle 316 Moderate

	5		3		8			
	1		9					6
				1			8	9
				9	4			
9	3			4			2	5
		1	5					
4	6			5				
1					2		7	
			4		7		5	

Sudoku

	2							
1	7		5	8				2
				9			8	1
		2		4	8			
	6	4				9	7	
			7	3		5		
5	4			2				
2				7	5		1	6
							4	

		9			8			
	6			7	9	8		5
8			3	5			6	
				5	6			4
2		8	1					
	1			3	6			2
3		6	4	2			9	
			5			1		

Sudoku

Puzzle 319   Moderate

9	6		3	8				2
	2					6		
4							1	
2			4		3			
		9				2		
			6		2			5
	7							1
		6					8	
8				7	9		6	3

Puzzle 320   Moderate

		7					5	4
	9		5				7	6
				2		1	8	
			2					
5	6						1	7
					8			
	7	4		6				
2	8				3		9	
9	3					6		

Sudoku

Puzzle 321 Moderate

		8		9	6			7
				8			3	5
	4				7	1		
7		3						
			3	6	9			
						2		3
		1	8				9	
9	8			5				
4			9	1		7		

Puzzle 322 Moderate

			2		4			
		8	5	7		6		
5				8			2	
8	2		7			1		
1								6
		4			8		3	2
	5			6				4
		6		2	5	9		
			8		3			

Sudoku

Puzzle 323 — Moderate

		2		1			3	
1		6		8		5		
	5						9	
					4		5	7
			8		5			
6	3		7					
	4						6	
		7		4		1		9
	6			9		4		

Puzzle 324 — Moderate

					4			1
8		4			5			
		6	1		7			
6							9	
5	3		2		8		6	7
	9							2
			8		3	2		
			5			3		6
4			7					

Sudoku

2		8	3				7	
		1		2				6
					1	8	9	
				6				3
		5	7		8	9		
4				3				
	8	4	2					
1				7		5		
	7					5	4	9

			9	2				
	4	1						
8	6				1			7
	1				4		9	5
		7		1		6		
6	9		5				2	
9			1				6	8
						4	7	
				5	8			

Puzzle 327 Moderate

			4		9			2
				5		1	9	
	1							5
4			5		1	7		
		2		3		5		
		7	6		8			4
5							6	
	6	9		7				
8			9		3			

Puzzle 328 Moderate

	4		7		6			1
				9		2		
	5		1				8	
	3				5	8		
7				8				2
		9	6				5	
	9				2		6	
		1		3				
5			9		1		2	

Sudoku

Puzzle 329 — Hard

			3		4		5	
4	1				2		9	
		5		9				6
			1			7		5
				6				
1		3			5			
3				4		5		
	7		8				3	4
	8		5		9			

Puzzle 330 — Hard

9		5		4				3
	7		9					1
		1			3			5
			2		7		4	
	6		4		8			
2			5			8		
5					6		2	
8				1		3		9

Puzzle 331   Hard

	5				1			2
		8	7			4		
			3	2			9	
				4		1		
4			1		9			3
		7		5				
	7			8	4			
		9			6	3		
8			2				4	

Puzzle 332   Hard

4			9			3		
9		8	1					
	5					6		
	2		6			8		
		4	8		1	2		
		1			2		4	
		9					3	
					5	1		7
		5			6			9

Sudoku

Puzzle 333 — Hard

Puzzle 334 — Hard

Sudoku

Puzzle 335   Hard

			4	9			2	
3	1						8	
9				1		6		3
	2				8			
8								5
		2					1	
1		5		3				8
	3						5	2
	7			8	5			

Puzzle 336   Hard

8							1	
5					3		9	
		3	7	9		2		
						9		1
	1			2			4	
4		5						
		9		6	1	7		
	7		8					9
	4							5

Puzzle 337 Hard

2	8		9					
	1					7		
	3	7	6					9
			7			1		
			2	4	8			
		6			5			
3					9	6	5	
		2					1	
					2		8	4

Puzzle 338 Hard

	2				6	4	9	
	4		1					
		5		9				
7	3				1	6		
				4				
		9	6				8	2
				6		5		
					3		7	
	1	2	5				6	

Sudoku

Puzzle 339 Hard

				9			1	7
	9		8		1	2		
		5						4
8					7	5		
				5				
		1	6					3
4						7		
		9	3		2		5	
3	6			8				

Puzzle 340 Hard

					8			1
		5			2			
				9		8		4
	7					5	6	
	8		1		9		2	
	3	4					1	
9		2		5				
			9			1		
6			8					

Puzzle 341   Hard

	3				1			
			4		5			8
						6	2	
1		3				8		
	4			1			3	
		2				5		4
	6	7						
4			8		7			
			3				9	

Puzzle 342   Hard

				8				
	1	2					6	
			7		4			9
	4	9			8		1	7
1				5				2
6	2			4		3	9	
2				8		5		
	8						9	7
				1				

Sudoku

Puzzle 343 — Hard

		4	8				5	
	2	9	1		5	3		
						7		
6		1	3					
			7	1	8			
					6	5		8
	5							
	8	6		9	4	3		
	4				1	9		

Puzzle 344 — Hard

	5	3						2
			7				8	
		2			5	9	3	
		4	5	7				
9				8				3
				6	1	4		
	4	7	8			1		
	6				7			
8						2	5	

Sudoku

Puzzle 345   Hard

2				5			6	
	8		2			9		
				7			8	4
	6	7			8	3		
				4				
		5	6			4	1	
3	4			8				
		2			5		3	
	5			6				7

Puzzle 346   Hard

		3	8		6			
9							8	3
					3			
5	3			1		9	7	
		2		9		3		
	6	9		5			2	1
			7					
3	1							6
			2		1	7		

Puzzle 347   Hard

5	6			3	1	4	7	
			8		6			1
2				9		5		
3				1				4
	8		3					7
6			9		4			
	9	4	1	8			6	5

Puzzle 348   Hard

1			9		3			
	2							9
	5			1			2	8
			2		6			4
	1			9			7	
8			1		5			
2	3			8			5	
6							8	
			6		1			3

Puzzle 349   Hard

		7				8		
	8				6	4		
3			9	8	4			
		9		6	3			
	6						1	
			2	1		7		
			3	4	7			5
	3	5					2	
		4				9		

Puzzle 350   Hard

						8		
			2		6	3		4
		2	4				9	7
2							1	
		9	7		5	2		
	3							5
6	2				4	1		
1		4	3		9			
		5						

Puzzle 351   Hard

		6						7
	4	9			7			3
			2	4			6	
		2	4	7	8			
			9	5	6	8		
	9			2	1			
2			5			3	7	
8						5		

Puzzle 352   Hard

6	1							
					5			
		9	4		6		7	
		1		7		5	6	3
		2				9		
7	9	5		3		1		
	4		1		2	8		
			3					
							4	1

Sudoku

Puzzle 353　　　　　　Hard

1			5					
		7			9		5	
							2	4
	8	6	7			2		
	2			9			3	
		4			3	6	8	
4	3							
	5		6			7		
					8			2

Puzzle 354　　　　　　Hard

					8			
	1	8	9					6
	3		4					9
		2			6			
1	6			3			9	8
			8			4		
5					9		7	
7					4	5	1	
			7					

Puzzle 355   Hard

		3	2		8		4	
	8			7				2
2					5			7
						4	9	
	6	1						
7			1					9
3				5			2	
	9		8		4	3		

Puzzle 356   Hard

			6	4		1		
3					7	5		2
	5						9	
	4							5
1	6			7			2	9
9							1	
	3						4	
8		1	5					7
		9		1	2			

Sudoku

Puzzle 357 — Hard

	3				7			
		7	6	8	3	4		
				2				
3		5				8	9	
	8			6			1	
	4	2				6		7
				1				
		8	2	5	6	3		
			7				2	

Puzzle 358 — Hard

2		8						
	1	5	4		6			
4				9	2			
3					5		6	
	5			4			1	
	7		8					2
			5	3				7
			6		1	9	2	
						1		5

Puzzle 359   Hard

				7				
			9		3	2		
9		7	2		5		4	
		8					2	1
		4		2		8		
6	9					4		
	4		7		8	6		9
		5	4		1			
				6				

Puzzle 360   Hard

8		9		7	3			
					2	3		
5				6		8		
3		7					8	
	4						7	
	8					6		4
		1		5				9
		6	2					
			4	1		5		2

Puzzle 361   Hard

	1							3
		2			5			
6		5		9		1		2
1		8						
	6		2		7		9	
						5		4
7		3		1		9		5
			7			3		
4							6	

Puzzle 362   Hard

	7	1	3	9	2			
8		4				9		
			5					
			6					3
	3		2		5		7	
2			1					
			4					
		7				1		9
			9	2	1	7	8	

Puzzle 363   Hard

		7		2				
5	8					6		7
			4				1	
	3			8	5			
		2	3		6	9		
			2	7			3	
	7				1			
8		5					4	9
				9		3		

Puzzle 364   Hard

5		8			7	4		
		6		2				
	7					9	3	
				6			2	4
			9		1			
6	8			5				
	1	3					9	
				3		8		
		4	7			2		3

Puzzle 365   Hard

					5			
2	9			7		1		
	6	7		1		3		
			9			8		
9			6		3			4
		2			1			
		8		3		5	9	
		4		9			2	8
			7					

Puzzle 366   Hard

		6						
3			1	6		8		2
7					3			
				2	7	1	5	
5								3
	8	2	4	3				
			5					8
2		3		4	8			1
					6			

Puzzle 367   Hard

			2			6		
5					6			2
	1	2					3	5
		7			3			
		3	1		2	9		
			8			7		
2	8					5	9	
3			5					4
		6			9			

Puzzle 368   Hard

	4		1		8			3
		2						8
				2			5	
		4	3				6	
8			5		9			4
	5				1	8		
	6			7				
4						5		
1			8		2		3	

Sudoku

Puzzle 369 — Hard

	7		8					3
					2			6
9				1				5
	1			4			8	
	8		2		1		6	
	3			8			4	
1				6				2
3		7						
8					3		9	

Puzzle 370 — Hard

				2			7	4
			3					
2		3	5			8		
					2	1		
6			7	5	8			2
		2	6					
		8			4	2		6
					6			
1	9			3				

Puzzle 371 Hard

7				4				
3					6		5	
		3	7					8
		4			8			1
	1						4	
6		2		8				
8			6	4				
	3	7						2
			5					7

Puzzle 372 Hard

		2				5		
	6			2			7	1
		7		5				4
2					3			6
			9	4	2			
1			8					5
9				6		4		
3	2			8			6	
		6				8		

Puzzle 373   Hard

8		7				3		
	6			3			7	9
	5							
5	2			6		9		
			1	8	5			
		6		4			8	5
							4	
6	1			7			2	
		3				6		1

Puzzle 374   Hard

	6				5			
9	3				8	2		
	2		3			9		
	4		6			7		
		7		9		3		
		2			1		6	
		3			2		9	
		9	1				5	3
			5				7	

Puzzle 375 Hard

2		6				7		
			6		9			
			5				8	3
	9		4			8	6	
		2		9		1		
	1	7			6		2	
6	5				4			
			9		8			
		9				3		8

Puzzle 376 Hard

		3		2			7	
	2	5			7			3
	6			9			5	
			2				4	8
3	8				1			
	7			5			6	
1			8			5	9	
	5			6		4		

Sudoku

Puzzle 377 Hard

	8		5		6		1	
	4			9				
1		3						8
			7	5		9		
		8				7		
	5		1	4				
2						1		9
				1			8	
	3		4		9		2	

Puzzle 378 Hard

			3		2	9		
	1				9			
5			6				7	
8		7					3	9
		3				2		
4	9					7		1
	7				5			6
			9				8	
		4	2		6			

Sudoku

Puzzle 379 — Hard

	2	3			9			1
			8			5		6
	5			7				
2				6		3	8	
	8	9		2				4
				4			9	
5		6			2			
8			7			6	5	

Puzzle 380 — Hard

						1	8	
		7			3			6
			4		1	5	2	
		3			6		4	
			7		4			
	2		8			9		
	9	8	1		7			
1			3			6		
	6	2						

194

Sudoku

Puzzle 381 Hard

		9		2	1		8	3
							7	
	8		6		5			
					2		4	1
3								8
1	5		4					
			2		4		6	
	7							
9	1		3	8		2		

Puzzle 382 Hard

		7			1	3		
	8			9			2	
5							6	
				4	3	5		
3			2		5			4
		1	9	6				
	1							9
	4			1			7	
		6	8			2		

Puzzle 383   Hard

2				5				
		5	4		2	7		
	8				3			
	2	7					5	
	6	1		9	8			
	9					1	3	
		8					2	
		9	5		1	4		
			9					7

Puzzle 384   Hard

		1		7		4		
				2	8		9	
8				4	5			
1	5		6					
	4						2	
					9		4	1
		5	4					7
	1		8	3				
		7		6		2		

Sudoku

Puzzle 385   Hard

			3	7			1	
8								
1	6				9	5		
		8			4		9	7
	2						6	
9	3		6			4		
		9	8				5	3
								4
	1			5	6			

Puzzle 386   Hard

5	7							
				3			5	
6		2	8					3
			2			3	8	
			4	7	8			
	2	6			5			
3					4	5		9
	6			1				
							4	2

197

Sudoku

Puzzle 387 — Hard

		9	6					
7			5					
	5			8	1	7		
5	4							6
	2						1	
1							3	4
		3	7	1			4	
					6			2
					9	8		

Puzzle 388 — Hard

							7	
4				9		3	5	8
	3				5			4
		9			7			5
	8			3			6	
2			6			8		
7			1				4	
3	1	4		2				9
	6							

Puzzle 389   Hard

9		4			7	5		
	7	1		6				
		5			9			
		6		4				5
8								2
5				3		8		
			1			4		
				5		3	8	
		3	4			9		7

Puzzle 390   Hard

2	7		5				1	
		3			2			4
				7	6			
7					3	9		
			4		3			
	2	1						5
		9	6					
8			2			4		
	4				1		5	8

Puzzle 391   Hard

	8							
	4	5	8	1				
9		2				1		8
		6		5				
2		8				9		3
				2		7		
3		7				2		4
				6	3	5	1	
							9	

Puzzle 392   Hard

			1	7		6		
8	6							7
					4		2	
	7			6	2			8
		9				2		
6			5	9			3	
	8		7					
9							4	5
		2		1	5			

Sudoku

Puzzle 393 — Hard

		9			4		7	
		1			7		3	
	6				3			
5		3			2		9	
6								1
	1		8			5		4
			7				4	
	2		6			8		
9		6			1			

Puzzle 394 — Hard

4			3			7		
5			6				1	
		9	7					
					8	3	4	6
			5		2			
1	6	7	9					
					7	5		
	9				6			1
		4			9			2

Puzzle 395 Hard

	7	6		5				
		4	6					5
							1	
5				7	9		8	
	2						7	
	8		5	4				2
	3							
7					1	6		
				2		4	9	

Puzzle 396 Hard

				2		4	9	3
6							7	
		2			3			6
9	2							4
		4		1		9		
7							5	1
2			7			6		
	7							9
4	8	9		5				

Puzzle 397   Hard

			2			5	8	4
4			1			2		
					4		6	
		6		8	2	7		
				3				
		5	9	1		8		
	4		6					
		8			1			2
6	9	1			5			

Puzzle 398   Hard

	1	6						7
7				6	9	4		
8	4						2	
		1	8		6			
				4				
			5		3	1		
	5						1	9
		4	6	9				8
2						7	6	

Puzzle 399 Hard

		6						7
	7					8	4	6
				1			5	
		4	2	8				
		2	5		1	4		
				3	9	7		
	6			4				
3	4	7					1	
5						2		

Puzzle 400 Hard

2	6		4		7			5
		4						
			8	5				
					6	2	9	7
1								8
3	7	2	5					
				4	3			
						7		
4			7		2		1	6

Sudoku

Puzzle 401   Hard

	5				4			
		9		2				6
		3	5			7		
	7		6				5	3
		1				9		
6	9				8		1	
		4			7	3		
8				4		1		
			2				9	

Puzzle 402   Hard

9	3		6				2	
5			2					8
			4		1			
						8		9
	8			6			1	
6		1						
			8		6			
3					4			6
	7				2		8	3

Puzzle 403 Hard

		2			4		9	
9				3				
5			7	9		8		
3						7	4	
4				7				8
	2	8						1
		1		4	6			3
				2				9
	4		5			6		

Puzzle 404 Hard

2			3	7				
	8				4	6		
			2		6	4		
6							1	
1	9			3			4	7
	3							6
		3	7		2			
		1	8				9	
				1	3			4

Puzzle 405   Hard

	5		4		2		1	
7				8	6			5
		3						9
	4					5		
6								4
		2					7	
9						7		
2			5	4				8
	3		8		9		5	

Puzzle 406   Hard

				5		4		
					1	5	7	
		6	8	3	4			
1		4			6			
2								6
			4			8		1
			3	8	7	6		
	5	8	1					
		2		4				

Puzzle 407   Hard

			9			1		2
	2			7			3	
4				1		6		
		5				7		
8			4		6			9
		2				3		
		9		2				3
	8			6			1	
1		3			5			

Puzzle 408   Hard

						9		7
	7	3			4			
		9			1			4
	4	8			3		7	
9								2
	5		9			8	4	
2			5			7		
			6			4	2	
8		5						

Puzzle 409   Hard

4	1							5
	9	8	3			4	7	
		7						
			5				6	
5			1		8			9
	4				2			
						3		
	8	1			7	9	5	
7							4	2

Puzzle 410   Hard

	6				1		9	7
3							4	6
			9		6			
4			5	9		2		
		7		1	3			5
			6		4			
6	7							8
5	2		7				3	

Sudoku

Puzzle 411 — Hard

					9			2
	8		1	5		7		
				2			1	6
1							4	
		8		4		9		
	9							8
7	3			9				
		4		6	1		2	
6			8					

Puzzle 412 — Hard

7				1				5
2					8	3		
		3	5				8	
	4					7		
			7	6	5			
		7					2	
	9				2	5		
		2	6					8
6				8				9

Sudoku

							5	9
3								
6	9	1	4					7
			7			2		
		9	1		5			
	6		3					
7				2	6	8	1	
								5
2	1							

		9		2				1
	2		9					
		8				2		4
		3	8		2			
7			1	3	9			2
			6		7	5		
6		5				3		
					3		7	
3				6		4		

Puzzle 415　　　　　　　　**Hard**

	1	6				2		
			4			1		9
8	4		1			5		
			8					
3			9	2	1			5
					5			
		8			3		2	1
1		2			6			
		3				8	7	

Puzzle 416　　　　　　　　**Hard**

		4			3	6		
			2					4
2	7	9	4					
		5			7	3		9
				6				
8		7	9			2		
					5	9	3	1
7					1			
		3	8			4		

Sudoku

Puzzle 417   Hard

								5
	4	6			8	9		
	5		3			1		
			8		1	7		
6				7				8
		3	4		6			
		9			5		3	
		7	2			5	4	
2								

Puzzle 418   Hard

						7		8
			4	8				
4			7			1		2
			3	9		2		
	3			6			7	
		5		1	8			
8		1			2			9
				7	9			
5		9						

Sudoku

Puzzle 419 — Hard

		6			5		4	7
								9
			2		4	3		
		5		3	8			
	8	2		7		6	5	
			4	5		1		
		4	9		7			
3								
7	6		5			4		

Puzzle 420 — Hard

	5							2
2	6		1	4			5	
				5				
3			6		5		2	
	2			1			9	
	4		7		8			5
				7				
	7			6	2		4	8
9							6	

Sudoku

Puzzle 421 — Hard

			5	2				
			7	9		2	6	
8			1				5	
		8						3
4		1		6		9		8
7						5		
	1				5			6
	8	9		4	1			
				7	2			

Puzzle 422 — Hard

			2					6
				3		1		8
		5	6				4	
		2			1	4		3
	9						6	
8		3	5			2		
	5				4	9		
1		4		2				
3				6				

215

Puzzle 423   Hard

	4		1				3	
		6		3				9
	9	7						5
			7				2	
4			6		8			1
	7				4			
5						3	1	
7				5		6		
	3				6		9	

Puzzle 424   Hard

8		7		2				9
		3			4	7		
	1			8				
			5			4		
7								5
		6			2			
				5			6	
		4	8				9	
9				3		5		1

Sudoku

		1	4				5	
		9			6			
2	4		7					
	9			6		5		
5		3		8		4		1
		6		3			2	
					2		8	7
			1			6		
	1				5	2		

	9	1	8					
5					9			7
2					5		3	
1						2	8	
	4						6	
	2	9						1
	1		6					8
9			3					4
					8	6	5	

Puzzle 427 Hard

8			3					
		3		2				
6		2	1	5				9
				9			5	
1	3						6	8
	5			8				
9				6	5	7		1
				3		9		
					7			6

Puzzle 428 Hard

8		4				7		
	5			3				8
	9	3						4
					5			9
			6	4	1			
7			3					
3						2	7	
6				8			1	
		1				9		6

Sudoku

	3	2		8	4			9
			2					
9					6		2	
6	4							
7	8			3			9	2
							8	5
	7		4					3
					3			
3			9	1		8	7	

					7		6	
				6		3	4	8
			9				2	
	8					7	3	1
1				8				4
6	4	3					5	
	9				5			
5	6	1		7				
	3		4					

219

Puzzle 431   Hard

9	3							
	8	1			3	5		
	2		5		1			
			8				4	5
		3		6		2		
5	4				2			
			1		6		5	
		8	9			1	3	
							8	9

Puzzle 432   Hard

7	5			6				1
				4		3	6	
	8							
	7				3	2		
	6		8		4		1	
		1	2				8	
							5	
	1	8		9				
2				8			3	4

Sudoku

Puzzle 433 — Hard

5		1	7			8		
					5			4
	6		3				7	
			9				5	2
		5				1		
2	8				3			
	9				7		4	
3			2					
		7			8	3		9

Puzzle 434 — Hard

		4		9	3			
			6				2	
7	1					4		
2							1	9
4			2		1			6
6	3							4
		2					4	8
	8				5			
			3	8		7		

Puzzle 435   Hard

	1			5				2
2					1	5		
		9	4	2		7		
							3	9
		7		4				
4	8							
		2		7	5	8		
		3	8					1
8				9			6	

Puzzle 436   Hard

				4		6	9	
					6		8	7
			9		7	4		
		5				8		4
8				5				6
1		9				2		
		8	2		3			
5	2		6					
	3	6		7				

Sudoku

Puzzle 437 — Hard

	2	7		4				
6	4		3		8			
		3			6		7	
						4		6
		6				9		
5		8						
	3		8			1		
			7		5		4	3
				1		7	9	

Puzzle 438 — Hard

		1				4	7	
					8			
6		3	2	9				
8				6	5			
	5			7			3	
			4	2				1
				8	2	3		4
		6						
	4	2				1		

Puzzle 439 Hard

6		7		9				
							5	
			7		4	6		
		3			1	4		
		8	5	4	3	7		
		5	2			8		
		4	8		6			
	2							
				7		5		1

Puzzle 440 Hard

4	7							
			9					
			3	7	4			2
	4			1		6		3
		2				9		
6		3		8			7	
8			5	9	3			
					8			
							8	1

Sudoku

7					5		2	
3	1			8	4			7
					7	3		
2					1			
		8		3		6		
			8					3
		3	4					
6			5	7			3	8
	5		1					4

8		6	3					9
7		2						
				6				
		9	8	5		4		
	1						6	
		7		9	3	5		
				2				
						3		1
4					9	7		5

Puzzle 443   Hard

	9	2				5		
			9		8			4
4		7						
	8				5	1		
			3		7			
		6	1				8	
						6		3
7			5		1			
		4				9	5	

Puzzle 444   Hard

							5	1
	9	7	2	5				
4				6				
			3	8				9
	8		9		5		4	
3			6	1				
				9				2
			2	4	3	6		
5	7							

Sudoku

Puzzle 445 — Hard

					3	9		
		2		4		1		5
	5		2	8				
	4		6					
	7	1				3	6	
					1		2	
				6	7		4	
7		5		9		8		
		4	3					

Puzzle 446 — Hard

		9			1	4		
		8				9	6	
	2		9		8			
2					3	7		9
				8				
1		5	4					3
			7		2		3	
	4	6				2		
		2	3			1		

Puzzle 447 Hard

3			6					
					4		7	2
				3			9	1
4		5	3				1	
		9				7		
	6				8	4		5
6	8			7				
2	9		8					
					6			4

Puzzle 448 Hard

	1		4			3		
	5				9			4
		9		1	8			6
	9				2		4	
	8		3				6	
9			6	5		7		
4			8				2	
		1			3		8	

Sudoku

Puzzle 449 — Hard

4	6		9	3				
		2						
		9		1				3
		6	3				7	
	9		7		4		5	
	7				1	3		
2				6		9		
						5		
				8	7		2	1

Puzzle 450 — Hard

9					3		5	
	1						2	
2			1		7	8		
6			4					
7	5			6			4	1
					5			8
		2	9		1			3
	6						8	
	7		2					5

Puzzle 451 — Hard

1			3				7	
6		7		8				
	2							1
	5			4		2		
	6	8		1	3			
	4		9			5		
4							8	
				1		4		9
	8				9			5

Puzzle 452 — Hard

			3	8				
		5		4				8
8		9	2				6	
		3						1
	9	1				8	5	
6						2		
	6				2	9		4
4				6		1		
				7	1			

Sudoku

Puzzle 453   Hard

							4	
1	7		2	4	8			
5			3	1				
	3					4		8
		2				5		
4		9					7	
			8	7				3
			1	6	4		8	5
	8							

Puzzle 454   Hard

	2			8			4	
				1	2			
3	8				9			5
6		4			7		1	
	9		2			3		8
9			1				3	4
			7	6				
	1			5			2	

231

Puzzle 455   Hard

	1	5	2					
				4				
	6	4			5			7
6		3	5		7			
				9				
			3		2	8		9
9			8			6	7	
				2				
					3	4	5	

Puzzle 456   Hard

		5				2		
	8		7		5	4		1
					9			7
	2		8		3		1	
				2				
	1		9		6		5	
8			3					
9		2	6		1		3	
		7				9		

Sudoku

Puzzle 457   Hard

7						6		
					6		7	
			8	9	7	1		
9			3			2	5	
	8						4	
	4	5			1			9
		4	5	6	3			
	2		7					
		6						8

Puzzle 458   Hard

2			8	4	6			
5		9		7				
			9				4	2
	9							6
		2				9		
1							2	
6	5				7			
				5		3		8
			6	2	1			4

233

Puzzle 459 Hard

	2							6
8	4		9	1				
	9			6		8		
	7				9			
		9	1	4	6	7		
			7				4	
		4		7			5	
				8	4		2	7
5							6	

Puzzle 460 Hard

8			2		7			5
	1		6				8	
2			8		3		4	
	9	4						
				6				
						1	2	
	8		5		6			1
	6				2		3	
5			7		9			4

Sudoku

Puzzle 461 — Hard

3	8				2			
					6	5		
	4		1				7	
	7	8		4		3		
		4				7		
		1		7		2	9	
	5				8		6	
		2	3					
			5				2	1

Puzzle 462 — Hard

	2				1		5	
6				2				
7	4	3						
8			6	7				
		4	2		3	6		
				5	9			7
						9	6	3
				9				2
	5		3				8	

Puzzle 463   Hard

		9	7		2		6	
			8				9	
8				9				5
	3				1			8
		4				7		
5			9				2	
4				1				3
	8				6			
	2		4		8	5		

Puzzle 464   Hard

			9		3	2		7
	5	1					6	
						8	5	
			2	6				
	2		3		9		4	
				4	7			
	8	3						
	1					9	8	
5		4	1		2			

Sudoku

Puzzle 465 — Hard

	1					4		3
2				3	8	1		
			9	1				
	6				1			
		7	6	8	5	2		
			4				7	
				2	3			
		8	1	4				6
3		1					5	

Puzzle 466 — Hard

					7			
		4		8		7	6	2
	7		9					4
		5			4		8	
7				2				3
	8		3			9		
1					6		7	
6	3	2		4		8		
			8					

237

Puzzle 467   Hard

7		4				9	6	
	8							
6			4				7	5
				2			4	
		3	9	7	1	5		
	2			8				
2	1				8			3
							9	
	5	6				1		7

Puzzle 468   Hard

					3			
	4					5		
9		8		5	2		6	
		5	2					4
	3	6				8	7	
2					4	6		
	8		7	1		4		9
		4					1	
			3					

Sudoku

Puzzle 469   Hard

9		6	5					
					3			
	1		6		9	2	7	
5	9				4			1
				2				
7			3				2	4
	3	4	1		8		6	
			7					
					6	1		2

Puzzle 470   Hard

7			2					
	2					8		3
	4			3			5	
			5	4			9	6
			6		8			
6	5			2	7			
	7			5			3	
4		9					2	
					4			1

239

Puzzle 471 Hard

7			2				9	
3			1		8			
		6	3				7	5
					4			7
		4				5		
9			7					
5	2				7	4		
			5		6			2
	3				1			9

Puzzle 472 Hard

3				7	9	5		
		7	3				4	9
1				9			5	6
		2		5		1		
4	7			2				8
5	4				6	3		
		1	7	3				5

Sudoku

Puzzle 473 — Hard

					2		
				7		9	3
		1	9	4				6
3								9
2		4	6	7	9	3		8
6								4
7				2	8	9		
4	6		5					
		9						

Puzzle 474 — Hard

						2	1	
	9				4		7	
	7	2	1	6				
6			9		8			
		9		1		6		
			6		5			3
				8	7	3	9	
	3		2				4	
	5	8						

241

Puzzle 475 Hard

7	1				5			
9			2					1
		4						
3			8	6			1	
		8	4		1	7		
	4			2	9			3
						4		
8					2			7
			3				5	9

Puzzle 476 Hard

7						6		
			9		1		4	
			6		2		7	3
1	6		8			4		
				1				
		5			3		6	7
8	3		1		9			
	7		5		4			
		4						8

Sudoku

Puzzle 477 — Hard

4	7		9					
			1					4
		5	7		6	3		
1					7	4		8
				8				
9		7	3					5
		2	4		1	8		
3					9			
					2		1	6

Puzzle 478 — Hard

			4		7			
4		8	5				9	
	5			1	8		4	
		1				2		
2				5				6
		6				5		
	2		6	8			3	
	6				1	9		5
			7		9			

243

Puzzle 479 Hard

7					8			6
			1				8	4
			2				3	
	2		4	7				9
		8		9		6		
9				1	3		4	
	4				1			
2	9				4			
1			6					8

Puzzle 480 Hard

							8	9
		9	7					2
	8		4			1		
		7		4			5	6
				6				
4	6			3		2		
		8			6		7	
1					9	3		
3	7							

Sudoku

Puzzle 481 — Hard

			3			1		
				6				8
	5		8	4		7	2	
	3	4						
1		7				2		6
						3	8	
	4	8		2	9		7	
5				7				
		9			6			

Puzzle 482 — Hard

								9
6			7		8			4
		1	3		9	2		
		3			4			8
		6		8		5		
4			1			7		
		8	6		3	9		
2			8		1			7
9								

Puzzle 483 Hard

			7				9	6
3					1		7	
		6		4		1		
2	5							
	4		8		7		6	
							8	3
		7		1		6		
	1		4					9
8	2				3			

Puzzle 484 Hard

	3						6	
4				1				8
					6	5		9
	8							5
3	5	4				9	8	2
9							7	
5		8	7					
2				4				1
	1						5	

Puzzle 485 Hard

6			1				2	
		7	9		3			
	3		2	4				8
3	9							
	1					3		
							4	6
2				3	7		1	
		4			8	5		
	5				1			7

Puzzle 486 Hard

		9					1	
			8	5	4			2
		2			1			7
3					5		7	
		4				2		
	2		6					3
4			5			7		
5			1	3	8			
	8					9		

247

Puzzle 487   Hard

			3					6
		5		6			9	8
1	9			2				
		1	4					
	6						2	
					3	8		
				3			1	9
7	5			8		3		
2					7			

Puzzle 488   Hard

6							8	
	4			3		5		
	9	3	8		4			
5			4				7	
				7				
	1				2			3
			1		9	7	5	
		9		8			3	
	6							2

Sudoku

Puzzle 489 — Hard

				7	5	8		
			3			7		
			1			3	5	2
8			2			6	4	
				4				
	5	7			3			1
3	9	4			2			
		8			6			
		5	7	9				

Puzzle 490 — Hard

	2						1	
9						4		
	1	4	8				9	
5				8				
	6	2	9	4	5	1	8	
				2				7
	8					3	2	4
		9						5
	5						3	

Solutions

1.

9	5	4	2	6	3	7	1	8
7	3	2	1	4	8	6	9	5
1	6	8	9	7	5	2	4	3
2	8	9	7	5	6	4	3	1
6	7	5	3	1	4	8	2	9
4	1	3	8	2	9	5	7	6
3	4	6	5	9	7	1	8	2
8	2	7	6	3	1	9	5	4
5	9	1	4	8	2	3	6	7

2.

8	1	6	9	3	7	2	4	5
4	2	9	6	5	1	7	8	3
5	7	3	2	8	4	9	1	6
1	5	7	8	4	9	6	3	2
9	6	2	1	7	3	8	5	4
3	8	4	5	2	6	1	9	7
6	3	8	4	1	2	5	7	9
7	9	5	3	6	8	4	2	1
2	4	1	7	9	5	3	6	8

3.

8	4	6	5	2	3	7	1	9
2	5	7	6	1	9	3	4	8
9	1	3	8	4	7	2	6	5
7	6	5	1	8	2	4	9	3
1	9	8	7	3	4	5	2	6
3	2	4	9	5	6	8	7	1
5	8	2	4	9	1	6	3	7
4	7	9	3	6	8	1	5	2
6	3	1	2	7	5	9	8	4

4.

8	7	4	5	1	3	6	9	2
2	5	6	4	9	8	3	7	1
1	9	3	7	2	6	8	4	5
7	3	2	8	5	4	9	1	6
6	8	1	2	7	9	5	3	4
5	4	9	3	6	1	2	8	7
4	1	8	6	3	2	7	5	9
9	6	5	1	8	7	4	2	3
3	2	7	9	4	5	1	6	8

5.

1	3	2	7	5	6	8	9	4
4	5	7	9	8	2	1	3	6
6	8	9	3	1	4	2	7	5
5	9	3	2	6	1	7	4	8
7	6	1	4	9	8	5	2	3
2	4	8	5	7	3	6	1	9
3	1	6	8	4	7	9	5	2
9	7	4	6	2	5	3	8	1
8	2	5	1	3	9	4	6	7

6.

5	1	3	4	7	6	9	8	2
8	9	7	2	5	3	4	6	1
2	6	4	1	8	9	3	7	5
1	3	5	6	9	8	7	2	4
6	8	2	7	3	4	1	5	9
4	7	9	5	1	2	6	3	8
9	4	6	3	2	5	8	1	7
3	2	1	8	4	7	5	9	6
7	5	8	9	6	1	2	4	3

7.

6	3	1	9	7	2	8	4	5
2	7	5	6	8	4	9	3	1
9	8	4	5	1	3	7	6	2
5	2	3	1	9	8	6	7	4
1	6	9	4	2	7	5	8	3
7	4	8	3	5	6	1	2	9
8	9	2	7	3	1	4	5	6
3	1	6	8	4	5	2	9	7
4	5	7	2	6	9	3	1	8

8.

2	3	5	1	8	4	9	7	6
9	4	1	7	3	6	5	8	2
6	8	7	5	2	9	3	1	4
5	7	6	3	9	2	1	4	8
4	9	8	6	1	5	7	2	3
3	1	2	4	7	8	6	9	5
1	6	3	2	4	7	8	5	9
7	2	9	8	5	3	4	6	1
8	5	4	9	6	1	2	3	7

9.

5	7	9	1	8	6	2	3	4
1	3	2	5	4	7	8	9	6
6	4	8	3	9	2	7	5	1
9	2	7	6	3	8	4	1	5
4	8	6	7	5	1	9	2	3
3	5	1	9	2	4	6	7	8
7	6	5	8	1	9	3	4	2
2	9	3	4	6	5	1	8	7
8	1	4	2	7	3	5	6	9

Solutions

10.

2	6	3	5	7	4	8	1	9
1	4	9	6	8	2	3	7	5
7	5	8	3	1	9	2	6	4
4	9	1	7	5	3	6	2	8
3	2	6	1	4	8	9	5	7
5	8	7	9	2	6	4	3	1
6	3	5	4	9	7	1	8	2
8	1	4	2	6	5	7	9	3
9	7	2	8	3	1	5	4	6

11.

6	4	1	9	3	5	8	2	7
8	2	5	7	6	4	3	1	9
9	3	7	2	1	8	6	5	4
7	6	3	5	9	2	4	8	1
2	8	9	1	4	6	7	3	5
5	1	4	8	7	3	9	6	2
3	5	2	4	8	7	1	9	6
1	7	6	3	2	9	5	4	8
4	9	8	6	5	1	2	7	3

12.

4	1	8	2	5	6	3	7	9
5	3	2	7	9	8	6	1	4
6	7	9	3	4	1	2	5	8
3	2	7	5	1	4	8	9	6
8	5	1	9	6	2	4	3	7
9	4	6	8	7	3	5	2	1
1	8	5	6	3	7	9	4	2
2	9	4	1	8	5	7	6	3
7	6	3	4	2	9	1	8	5

13.

4	5	7	3	9	8	2	1	6
3	8	2	7	1	6	5	4	9
9	1	6	5	4	2	8	3	7
6	7	1	4	3	5	9	2	8
2	9	5	6	8	1	3	7	4
8	4	3	9	2	7	6	5	1
1	6	8	2	7	3	4	9	5
7	3	4	8	5	9	1	6	2
5	2	9	1	6	4	7	8	3

14.

8	9	7	5	1	3	2	6	4
6	1	2	4	9	7	3	8	5
3	5	4	2	6	8	9	1	7
4	7	9	1	2	5	6	3	8
1	2	8	6	3	4	7	5	9
5	6	3	8	7	9	1	4	2
9	4	1	3	8	2	5	7	6
2	3	5	7	4	6	8	9	1
7	8	6	9	5	1	4	2	3

15.

2	8	4	9	6	1	7	5	3
7	1	3	4	5	8	9	2	6
9	6	5	3	2	7	4	1	8
5	7	6	1	9	4	3	8	2
1	3	9	7	8	2	6	4	5
4	2	8	5	3	6	1	7	9
6	5	7	2	1	9	8	3	4
8	4	2	6	7	3	5	9	1
3	9	1	8	4	5	2	6	7

16.

4	5	7	3	1	9	8	2	6
9	2	6	4	8	5	7	3	1
8	3	1	7	2	6	5	4	9
6	7	5	8	9	2	4	1	3
1	4	8	6	3	7	2	9	5
3	9	2	5	4	1	6	7	8
5	8	9	2	7	3	1	6	4
7	1	4	9	6	8	3	5	2
2	6	3	1	5	4	9	8	7

17.

4	1	5	2	3	6	8	7	9
3	2	8	9	7	1	6	4	5
9	7	6	4	5	8	1	2	3
5	9	4	8	1	7	3	6	2
8	6	1	3	2	4	9	5	7
2	3	7	6	9	5	4	1	8
7	5	3	1	6	9	2	8	4
6	8	9	7	4	2	5	3	1
1	4	2	5	8	3	7	9	6

18.

3	4	9	5	8	6	1	7	2
8	2	7	1	4	3	9	5	6
5	6	1	9	2	7	3	4	8
1	7	4	8	9	2	6	3	5
2	3	5	6	7	4	8	1	9
9	8	6	3	1	5	4	2	7
7	9	8	4	5	1	2	6	3
4	5	3	2	6	8	7	9	1
6	1	2	7	3	9	5	8	4

Solutions

19.

9	7	1	8	4	6	5	2	3
3	5	4	7	2	9	8	6	1
2	6	8	1	5	3	9	7	4
6	9	3	5	8	4	7	1	2
1	2	5	6	9	7	3	4	8
4	8	7	3	1	2	6	5	9
5	3	9	4	7	1	2	8	6
8	4	6	2	3	5	1	9	7
7	1	2	9	6	8	4	3	5

20.

1	9	5	7	6	4	2	3	8
4	3	8	5	2	9	7	1	6
6	2	7	8	3	1	4	5	9
7	5	3	1	4	6	9	8	2
9	4	6	3	8	2	1	7	5
8	1	2	9	5	7	6	4	3
2	8	9	4	1	3	5	6	7
5	7	4	6	9	8	3	2	1
3	6	1	2	7	5	8	9	4

21.

7	1	8	9	4	3	2	6	5
2	9	3	1	6	5	8	4	7
6	5	4	8	2	7	9	3	1
4	8	6	7	9	1	5	2	3
3	2	9	4	5	6	7	1	8
5	7	1	2	3	8	6	9	4
1	6	5	3	8	2	4	7	9
9	3	2	5	7	4	1	8	6
8	4	7	6	1	9	3	5	2

22.

6	8	3	2	9	7	1	5	4
7	5	4	1	3	8	9	2	6
2	9	1	4	6	5	8	3	7
1	4	5	6	2	9	3	7	8
8	7	6	3	5	4	2	9	1
3	2	9	7	8	1	4	6	5
9	1	8	5	7	2	6	4	3
5	3	2	8	4	6	7	1	9
4	6	7	9	1	3	5	8	2

23.

6	5	4	2	1	8	3	9	7
2	9	7	5	3	6	8	1	4
8	3	1	4	9	7	5	6	2
5	6	8	9	2	1	7	4	3
7	2	3	6	4	5	9	8	1
4	1	9	7	8	3	2	5	6
9	8	2	1	7	4	6	3	5
1	7	5	3	6	9	4	2	8
3	4	6	8	5	2	1	7	9

24.

5	4	1	8	6	7	9	3	2
3	6	7	2	9	4	8	1	5
2	9	8	5	1	3	6	4	7
8	5	3	6	7	1	4	2	9
4	2	6	3	5	9	7	8	1
7	1	9	4	2	8	3	5	6
6	3	5	7	4	2	1	9	8
1	8	2	9	3	6	5	7	4
9	7	4	1	8	5	2	6	3

25.

3	8	7	9	4	1	2	5	6
4	1	9	2	6	5	7	8	3
5	6	2	3	8	7	9	1	4
7	3	4	5	2	8	1	6	9
6	5	8	4	1	9	3	7	2
2	9	1	6	7	3	8	4	5
1	4	3	7	5	2	6	9	8
9	7	5	8	3	6	4	2	1
8	2	6	1	9	4	5	3	7

26.

4	7	1	3	6	5	8	2	9
5	3	6	9	2	8	4	1	7
2	9	8	4	1	7	6	5	3
6	2	7	5	9	3	1	4	8
8	5	9	2	4	1	3	7	6
1	4	3	8	7	6	5	9	2
3	8	2	7	5	4	9	6	1
7	6	5	1	3	9	2	8	4
9	1	4	6	8	2	7	3	5

27.

4	1	9	6	8	3	5	2	7
8	6	3	5	2	7	4	9	1
7	5	2	1	9	4	8	3	6
2	4	1	9	3	6	7	8	5
6	3	8	4	7	5	9	1	2
5	9	7	2	1	8	6	4	3
1	8	6	3	5	9	2	7	4
9	2	5	7	4	1	3	6	8
3	7	4	8	6	2	1	5	9

Solutions

28.

6	7	2	3	9	5	1	4	8
5	4	9	1	6	8	7	3	2
3	1	8	7	2	4	9	6	5
1	6	3	8	4	9	2	5	7
9	2	5	6	1	7	3	8	4
4	8	7	5	3	2	6	9	1
7	3	4	2	5	6	8	1	9
2	9	6	4	8	1	5	7	3
8	5	1	9	7	3	4	2	6

29.

2	1	6	9	4	7	5	3	8
8	9	3	5	1	2	7	6	4
4	7	5	6	3	8	9	1	2
6	8	7	4	9	3	1	2	5
5	3	2	8	7	1	6	4	9
9	4	1	2	5	6	3	8	7
7	6	4	3	2	9	8	5	1
3	2	9	1	8	5	4	7	6
1	5	8	7	6	4	2	9	3

30.

7	4	5	3	2	9	1	6	8
1	6	9	7	5	8	2	3	4
8	2	3	6	1	4	5	9	7
4	3	2	5	8	7	6	1	9
9	5	7	2	6	1	4	8	3
6	1	8	9	4	3	7	5	2
3	7	4	1	9	6	8	2	5
5	9	1	8	7	2	3	4	6
2	8	6	4	3	5	9	7	1

31.

4	3	1	8	7	2	9	5	6
6	5	8	3	9	4	1	7	2
9	7	2	6	5	1	4	3	8
7	1	6	5	4	8	3	2	9
3	2	9	7	1	6	8	4	5
8	4	5	2	3	9	6	1	7
1	8	7	4	6	5	2	9	3
5	6	4	9	2	3	7	8	1
2	9	3	1	8	7	5	6	4

32.

1	6	9	4	8	3	7	2	5
5	4	3	7	2	1	8	9	6
8	2	7	5	9	6	3	1	4
4	3	2	6	5	7	1	8	9
6	7	8	9	1	2	5	4	3
9	5	1	8	3	4	2	6	7
3	8	5	1	4	9	6	7	2
7	1	4	2	6	5	9	3	8
2	9	6	3	7	8	4	5	1

33.

3	8	1	7	4	6	2	5	9
4	6	2	9	1	5	3	7	8
9	5	7	2	3	8	4	6	1
6	2	4	5	9	1	7	8	3
5	7	3	6	8	2	1	9	4
8	1	9	4	7	3	5	2	6
2	4	8	3	5	9	6	1	7
1	3	6	8	2	7	9	4	5
7	9	5	1	6	4	8	3	2

34.

1	7	2	3	4	8	5	6	9
3	5	4	2	6	9	8	7	1
8	6	9	7	5	1	3	2	4
2	1	3	5	9	6	7	4	8
5	8	7	4	1	2	9	3	6
4	9	6	8	3	7	1	5	2
9	2	8	6	7	5	4	1	3
6	3	5	1	8	4	2	9	7
7	4	1	9	2	3	6	8	5

35.

8	9	5	1	2	4	6	7	3
7	2	1	6	3	5	8	4	9
6	4	3	7	8	9	1	2	5
4	1	7	5	6	3	9	8	2
3	5	6	8	9	2	4	1	7
2	8	9	4	7	1	3	5	6
1	7	2	3	4	6	5	9	8
5	6	8	9	1	7	2	3	4
9	3	4	2	5	8	7	6	1

36.

5	1	7	3	2	6	9	4	8
4	3	2	9	1	8	6	7	5
6	8	9	7	5	4	2	1	3
1	2	3	4	6	5	7	8	9
8	7	5	1	3	9	4	2	6
9	4	6	2	8	7	3	5	1
7	6	4	8	9	1	5	3	2
2	9	8	5	4	3	1	6	7
3	5	1	6	7	2	8	9	4

Solutions

37.

5	6	8	7	4	3	1	9	2
1	9	7	2	8	6	5	3	4
3	4	2	5	9	1	8	6	7
7	3	9	6	1	2	4	8	5
4	8	1	9	7	5	6	2	3
6	2	5	4	3	8	7	1	9
8	7	3	1	2	4	9	5	6
9	1	6	3	5	7	2	4	8
2	5	4	8	6	9	3	7	1

38.

8	6	9	5	4	3	2	7	1
3	7	4	2	1	9	8	5	6
5	2	1	7	6	8	9	3	4
1	8	5	6	7	2	3	4	9
7	9	6	1	3	4	5	2	8
4	3	2	9	8	5	1	6	7
2	4	3	8	9	6	7	1	5
6	1	8	3	5	7	4	9	2
9	5	7	4	2	1	6	8	3

39.

4	2	3	6	8	5	1	7	9
5	7	8	1	2	9	6	3	4
1	9	6	7	4	3	5	2	8
2	5	1	8	7	4	3	9	6
3	4	7	5	9	6	2	8	1
6	8	9	3	1	2	7	4	5
7	1	2	9	5	8	4	6	3
8	6	4	2	3	1	9	5	7
9	3	5	4	6	7	8	1	2

40.

7	2	9	1	8	6	4	5	3
6	3	1	5	4	7	9	8	2
5	8	4	3	2	9	6	7	1
2	9	8	4	5	1	7	3	6
1	6	3	7	9	8	5	2	4
4	7	5	6	3	2	1	9	8
8	5	2	9	1	4	3	6	7
3	4	6	2	7	5	8	1	9
9	1	7	8	6	3	2	4	5

41.

5	2	1	4	3	8	6	9	7
3	9	8	7	1	6	4	5	2
7	6	4	5	2	9	8	3	1
1	3	5	8	4	2	7	6	9
6	7	2	9	5	3	1	8	4
4	8	9	6	7	1	3	2	5
9	1	3	2	6	7	5	4	8
8	5	7	3	9	4	2	1	6
2	4	6	1	8	5	9	7	3

42.

6	7	3	5	8	2	9	4	1
9	2	5	1	6	4	8	3	7
8	4	1	7	3	9	5	6	2
4	5	2	8	9	7	6	1	3
7	1	9	3	4	6	2	5	8
3	8	6	2	1	5	7	9	4
5	9	8	4	2	3	1	7	6
2	6	4	9	7	1	3	8	5
1	3	7	6	5	8	4	2	9

43.

6	5	4	1	9	8	2	7	3
1	9	3	7	2	6	5	8	4
8	2	7	4	5	3	6	9	1
2	3	6	8	1	4	9	5	7
4	7	9	2	6	5	1	3	8
5	8	1	9	3	7	4	6	2
9	4	5	3	8	2	7	1	6
7	1	8	6	4	9	3	2	5
3	6	2	5	7	1	8	4	9

44.

1	8	6	2	7	3	4	9	5
4	9	7	5	6	1	3	8	2
5	2	3	4	8	9	1	7	6
9	4	1	8	5	2	6	3	7
7	3	5	6	1	4	8	2	9
2	6	8	3	9	7	5	4	1
3	1	4	9	2	6	7	5	8
8	7	9	1	3	5	2	6	4
6	5	2	7	4	8	9	1	3

45.

6	2	1	9	4	7	3	5	8
4	8	9	5	2	3	1	6	7
7	5	3	8	1	6	4	2	9
1	6	8	4	3	9	5	7	2
5	3	2	7	6	1	9	8	4
9	4	7	2	8	5	6	1	3
2	1	6	3	7	4	8	9	5
3	7	5	1	9	8	2	4	6
8	9	4	6	5	2	7	3	1

Solutions

46.

6	4	2	1	8	3	5	9	7
7	1	3	9	5	6	2	8	4
8	5	9	4	7	2	6	1	3
2	3	8	7	4	5	9	6	1
5	7	6	3	1	9	8	4	2
4	9	1	6	2	8	7	3	5
3	8	7	5	6	4	1	2	9
9	2	5	8	3	1	4	7	6
1	6	4	2	9	7	3	5	8

47.

2	1	7	9	8	4	3	6	5
6	3	8	1	5	7	4	9	2
4	5	9	3	6	2	1	8	7
1	9	4	7	3	8	5	2	6
7	6	3	5	2	1	9	4	8
8	2	5	4	9	6	7	1	3
9	7	2	6	1	5	8	3	4
5	8	1	2	4	3	6	7	9
3	4	6	8	7	9	2	5	1

48.

1	8	3	4	6	2	9	7	5
7	6	2	9	1	5	3	8	4
5	9	4	3	7	8	6	2	1
3	5	9	7	2	6	1	4	8
8	4	7	1	5	3	2	6	9
6	2	1	8	9	4	7	5	3
2	3	5	6	8	9	4	1	7
9	7	6	5	4	1	8	3	2
4	1	8	2	3	7	5	9	6

49.

3	7	2	6	4	5	8	1	9
9	1	4	2	3	8	5	7	6
5	6	8	9	7	1	4	3	2
8	3	1	5	2	4	9	6	7
2	4	7	8	9	6	1	5	3
6	5	9	3	1	7	2	4	8
4	8	3	1	6	2	7	9	5
1	2	6	7	5	9	3	8	4
7	9	5	4	8	3	6	2	1

50.

2	5	4	7	1	6	9	3	8
8	6	1	2	9	3	7	4	5
9	7	3	4	8	5	1	2	6
4	1	2	9	6	8	3	5	7
7	3	5	1	4	2	8	6	9
6	9	8	3	5	7	2	1	4
3	2	6	8	7	4	5	9	1
5	8	9	6	2	1	4	7	3
1	4	7	5	3	9	6	8	2

51.

2	3	6	1	7	4	8	5	9
8	5	1	9	3	6	7	2	4
7	9	4	8	5	2	3	6	1
5	4	7	3	1	9	6	8	2
9	8	2	6	4	7	1	3	5
6	1	3	5	2	8	9	4	7
3	7	5	2	6	1	4	9	8
1	6	9	4	8	5	2	7	3
4	2	8	7	9	3	5	1	6

52.

5	9	4	1	6	7	8	2	3
7	8	1	3	2	4	6	9	5
2	6	3	5	9	8	1	7	4
3	5	2	4	1	9	7	8	6
1	4	8	6	7	2	5	3	9
9	7	6	8	5	3	2	4	1
6	2	9	7	4	5	3	1	8
4	3	5	2	8	1	9	6	7
8	1	7	9	3	6	4	5	2

53.

9	7	1	3	6	4	5	8	2
5	3	4	2	8	1	9	6	7
2	6	8	9	5	7	4	3	1
7	9	6	8	4	5	2	1	3
3	8	2	7	1	9	6	4	5
4	1	5	6	3	2	8	7	9
6	4	7	5	2	3	1	9	8
8	2	3	1	9	6	7	5	4
1	5	9	4	7	8	3	2	6

54.

4	6	8	7	9	3	5	2	1
9	2	1	5	6	4	3	7	8
7	5	3	8	2	1	6	9	4
6	7	4	2	3	8	9	1	5
8	1	9	4	5	7	2	3	6
5	3	2	9	1	6	8	4	7
3	4	7	6	8	2	1	5	9
2	9	6	1	4	5	7	8	3
1	8	5	3	7	9	4	6	2

Solutions

55.

4	1	8	2	3	7	6	5	9
5	7	2	6	9	1	4	3	8
3	6	9	4	5	8	2	7	1
9	2	3	7	4	5	1	8	6
7	4	5	1	8	6	3	9	2
6	8	1	9	2	3	5	4	7
2	9	7	5	1	4	8	6	3
8	5	6	3	7	2	9	1	4
1	3	4	8	6	9	7	2	5

56.

3	8	2	5	1	7	4	6	9
7	4	9	6	3	8	5	2	1
6	5	1	2	4	9	3	7	8
2	3	4	8	7	5	9	1	6
1	6	8	9	2	4	7	3	5
9	7	5	1	6	3	8	4	2
5	2	3	7	9	1	6	8	4
4	9	6	3	8	2	1	5	7
8	1	7	4	5	6	2	9	3

57.

3	7	4	1	8	5	6	9	2
2	6	1	9	7	3	4	5	8
8	5	9	2	4	6	3	1	7
6	9	3	7	5	1	2	8	4
1	8	7	4	9	2	5	6	3
5	4	2	3	6	8	1	7	9
9	2	6	8	1	4	7	3	5
4	1	8	5	3	7	9	2	6
7	3	5	6	2	9	8	4	1

58.

6	5	7	1	8	4	3	2	9
2	8	1	3	9	5	6	7	4
9	4	3	2	7	6	8	5	1
8	2	4	6	3	7	1	9	5
3	6	9	4	5	1	2	8	7
1	7	5	8	2	9	4	3	6
7	3	6	9	1	8	5	4	2
4	9	2	5	6	3	7	1	8
5	1	8	7	4	2	9	6	3

59.

2	8	7	1	5	9	4	6	3
5	1	4	3	7	6	8	2	9
6	9	3	4	2	8	5	1	7
7	3	8	2	9	4	6	5	1
1	4	5	7	6	3	9	8	2
9	6	2	8	1	5	7	3	4
4	5	1	6	3	7	2	9	8
8	2	6	9	4	1	3	7	5
3	7	9	5	8	2	1	4	6

60.

4	7	1	6	9	2	8	3	5
8	5	6	4	3	7	2	9	1
9	2	3	5	8	1	7	6	4
1	9	8	7	5	3	6	4	2
2	6	5	9	1	4	3	7	8
3	4	7	2	6	8	5	1	9
6	8	2	3	4	9	1	5	7
7	3	9	1	2	5	4	8	6
5	1	4	8	7	6	9	2	3

61.

9	5	8	4	2	3	7	6	1
7	2	4	1	8	6	9	3	5
3	6	1	9	7	5	2	4	8
5	8	6	3	1	7	4	2	9
4	7	2	5	6	9	8	1	3
1	3	9	2	4	8	5	7	6
8	1	3	7	5	2	6	9	4
2	9	5	6	3	4	1	8	7
6	4	7	8	9	1	3	5	2

62.

4	6	3	1	8	9	5	7	2
7	2	9	3	5	6	8	1	4
8	1	5	2	4	7	9	6	3
6	3	4	5	7	1	2	8	9
1	8	7	9	2	3	4	5	6
9	5	2	8	6	4	7	3	1
5	7	6	4	1	2	3	9	8
2	9	8	6	3	5	1	4	7
3	4	1	7	9	8	6	2	5

63.

3	2	6	1	7	5	9	8	4
8	9	1	6	4	2	5	7	3
7	4	5	3	9	8	1	6	2
1	5	4	9	8	7	2	3	6
9	7	3	4	2	6	8	1	5
6	8	2	5	3	1	7	4	9
4	1	9	8	5	3	6	2	7
2	3	8	7	6	9	4	5	1
5	6	7	2	1	4	3	9	8

Solutions

64.

2	8	4	1	7	6	3	5	9
3	5	1	9	2	4	7	8	6
9	6	7	5	3	8	1	2	4
1	3	8	2	4	9	5	6	7
6	9	5	3	8	7	2	4	1
7	4	2	6	5	1	9	3	8
4	7	3	8	1	5	6	9	2
5	1	6	4	9	2	8	7	3
8	2	9	7	6	3	4	1	5

65.

1	6	9	3	7	2	5	8	4
3	5	2	4	8	9	7	6	1
4	8	7	1	6	5	2	9	3
9	4	6	5	3	1	8	2	7
5	2	1	7	4	8	6	3	9
7	3	8	2	9	6	1	4	5
8	9	5	6	1	4	3	7	2
6	1	3	9	2	7	4	5	8
2	7	4	8	5	3	9	1	6

66.

4	2	7	9	5	3	1	8	6
5	6	3	1	2	8	4	9	7
8	1	9	7	4	6	5	2	3
3	9	2	4	6	7	8	5	1
6	7	5	8	9	1	3	4	2
1	4	8	2	3	5	6	7	9
2	8	4	3	1	9	7	6	5
9	5	1	6	7	4	2	3	8
7	3	6	5	8	2	9	1	4

67.

2	4	7	6	5	9	3	1	8
5	1	9	4	3	8	7	6	2
3	6	8	1	7	2	4	9	5
8	9	5	3	1	4	6	2	7
6	7	2	9	8	5	1	4	3
4	3	1	2	6	7	5	8	9
9	2	3	7	4	1	8	5	6
1	8	6	5	2	3	9	7	4
7	5	4	8	9	6	2	3	1

68.

2	7	4	6	8	5	9	1	3
1	5	9	3	4	2	6	7	8
3	6	8	9	1	7	2	4	5
8	4	3	7	6	1	5	9	2
9	2	6	8	5	4	7	3	1
5	1	7	2	9	3	8	6	4
4	3	2	5	7	6	1	8	9
6	9	5	1	3	8	4	2	7
7	8	1	4	2	9	3	5	6

69.

5	1	9	7	8	3	2	6	4
8	4	7	6	9	2	3	5	1
2	6	3	1	5	4	8	7	9
3	7	8	4	6	9	1	2	5
9	5	6	2	1	8	4	3	7
4	2	1	3	7	5	6	9	8
7	9	4	8	2	6	5	1	3
6	8	5	9	3	1	7	4	2
1	3	2	5	4	7	9	8	6

70.

4	6	9	3	1	8	2	5	7
3	1	5	4	2	7	9	6	8
2	7	8	5	6	9	4	3	1
1	9	2	6	8	3	7	4	5
6	3	7	2	4	5	8	1	9
5	8	4	7	9	1	3	2	6
8	5	3	1	7	4	6	9	2
7	4	6	9	5	2	1	8	3
9	2	1	8	3	6	5	7	4

71.

6	9	8	1	2	5	4	3	7
1	3	4	9	6	7	5	8	2
5	7	2	4	3	8	9	1	6
4	5	7	2	8	6	1	9	3
3	2	1	5	9	4	7	6	8
8	6	9	3	7	1	2	5	4
7	4	3	6	1	9	8	2	5
9	8	6	7	5	2	3	4	1
2	1	5	8	4	3	6	7	9

72.

7	4	1	5	2	3	9	6	8
2	6	9	4	7	8	1	5	3
3	8	5	1	9	6	2	7	4
5	1	6	8	3	2	7	4	9
4	9	7	6	5	1	8	3	2
8	2	3	9	4	7	6	1	5
9	3	8	7	6	4	5	2	1
6	5	4	2	1	9	3	8	7
1	7	2	3	8	5	4	9	6

Solutions

73.

5	2	7	1	9	3	6	8	4
6	3	9	8	4	5	2	7	1
4	1	8	7	2	6	3	5	9
3	4	5	9	1	2	8	6	7
8	6	1	3	5	7	9	4	2
7	9	2	6	8	4	5	1	3
1	7	6	5	3	9	4	2	8
2	8	3	4	6	1	7	9	5
9	5	4	2	7	8	1	3	6

74.

6	2	5	1	7	3	4	9	8
4	3	9	2	8	5	1	7	6
1	7	8	9	4	6	3	2	5
3	5	4	8	2	9	6	1	7
9	8	1	6	3	7	5	4	2
7	6	2	5	1	4	8	3	9
2	1	7	3	5	8	9	6	4
8	9	3	4	6	2	7	5	1
5	4	6	7	9	1	2	8	3

75.

8	9	2	6	5	3	1	7	4
1	4	3	7	9	2	5	6	8
7	6	5	1	8	4	2	3	9
9	8	4	2	7	6	3	1	5
6	5	7	9	3	1	8	4	2
3	2	1	8	4	5	6	9	7
4	1	6	5	2	7	9	8	3
5	3	8	4	1	9	7	2	6
2	7	9	3	6	8	4	5	1

76.

4	5	9	8	6	1	2	7	3
6	2	3	4	9	7	8	1	5
8	7	1	5	2	3	6	9	4
1	8	6	9	3	5	7	4	2
3	9	2	6	7	4	1	5	8
5	4	7	2	1	8	3	6	9
9	6	4	1	8	2	5	3	7
2	3	5	7	4	6	9	8	1
7	1	8	3	5	9	4	2	6

77.

8	7	3	6	5	9	2	4	1
2	1	9	8	4	7	3	6	5
4	6	5	1	3	2	7	9	8
5	4	1	9	7	8	6	3	2
3	8	6	2	1	4	5	7	9
9	2	7	3	6	5	1	8	4
1	9	8	7	2	3	4	5	6
7	5	2	4	9	6	8	1	3
6	3	4	5	8	1	9	2	7

78.

4	6	5	8	3	2	7	9	1
3	8	9	4	1	7	5	2	6
7	2	1	9	5	6	3	8	4
9	7	3	6	2	5	4	1	8
8	1	6	3	7	4	2	5	9
2	5	4	1	9	8	6	3	7
1	3	7	2	4	9	8	6	5
5	9	8	7	6	3	1	4	2
6	4	2	5	8	1	9	7	3

79.

7	2	5	1	3	8	4	6	9
8	3	6	5	9	4	1	7	2
9	4	1	2	7	6	3	5	8
2	5	9	6	4	3	7	8	1
1	6	3	8	2	7	5	9	4
4	7	8	9	5	1	6	2	3
3	9	2	4	6	5	8	1	7
5	1	4	7	8	9	2	3	6
6	8	7	3	1	2	9	4	5

80.

3	7	4	8	5	6	9	1	2
9	6	1	7	2	3	8	4	5
8	2	5	1	9	4	3	6	7
6	9	2	4	3	1	7	5	8
5	1	3	9	7	8	4	2	6
4	8	7	5	6	2	1	9	3
1	3	8	2	4	5	6	7	9
2	4	9	6	8	7	5	3	1
7	5	6	3	1	9	2	8	4

81.

9	3	5	2	8	7	4	1	6
4	7	6	9	1	5	2	3	8
2	8	1	3	6	4	5	7	9
3	4	2	8	7	6	1	9	5
6	9	8	1	5	2	3	4	7
1	5	7	4	9	3	6	8	2
8	2	3	6	4	9	7	5	1
7	1	4	5	2	8	9	6	3
5	6	9	7	3	1	8	2	4

Solutions

82.

3	9	8	6	5	7	1	2	4
5	6	4	3	1	2	8	9	7
7	1	2	4	8	9	6	3	5
4	7	9	8	3	1	5	6	2
6	3	5	9	2	4	7	8	1
8	2	1	5	7	6	9	4	3
2	5	6	7	4	8	3	1	9
9	4	3	1	6	5	2	7	8
1	8	7	2	9	3	4	5	6

83.

6	3	4	2	9	5	7	1	8
7	2	5	8	1	6	3	9	4
1	8	9	7	4	3	6	5	2
5	7	6	1	3	8	2	4	9
4	1	3	5	2	9	8	7	6
8	9	2	6	7	4	5	3	1
2	5	7	9	6	1	4	8	3
9	4	8	3	5	2	1	6	7
3	6	1	4	8	7	9	2	5

84.

2	9	3	5	1	4	7	6	8
8	7	4	2	6	3	5	1	9
6	5	1	9	8	7	4	3	2
1	8	7	6	4	5	9	2	3
3	2	9	1	7	8	6	5	4
5	4	6	3	9	2	8	7	1
4	3	5	7	2	9	1	8	6
9	6	2	8	5	1	3	4	7
7	1	8	4	3	6	2	9	5

85.

5	9	4	8	3	6	2	1	7
8	1	3	5	7	2	6	9	4
6	2	7	9	4	1	8	5	3
3	4	9	2	6	7	1	8	5
7	8	2	1	5	9	3	4	6
1	6	5	4	8	3	7	2	9
9	5	6	3	1	8	4	7	2
4	7	8	6	2	5	9	3	1
2	3	1	7	9	4	5	6	8

86.

2	5	9	6	1	8	3	7	4
6	1	7	4	3	5	9	2	8
4	8	3	7	2	9	5	1	6
8	4	1	3	6	7	2	9	5
7	3	5	8	9	2	6	4	1
9	2	6	5	4	1	7	8	3
3	6	2	9	8	4	1	5	7
1	7	8	2	5	3	4	6	9
5	9	4	1	7	6	8	3	2

87.

3	2	5	7	4	6	1	9	8
8	4	6	1	5	9	7	2	3
9	1	7	3	2	8	5	4	6
6	3	8	2	9	5	4	1	7
1	9	4	8	3	7	2	6	5
5	7	2	4	6	1	8	3	9
7	6	9	5	1	2	3	8	4
2	8	3	9	7	4	6	5	1
4	5	1	6	8	3	9	7	2

88.

4	9	8	2	7	6	1	5	3
1	5	7	4	3	8	6	9	2
3	2	6	1	5	9	7	8	4
5	1	4	9	2	3	8	7	6
8	3	9	7	6	1	4	2	5
6	7	2	5	8	4	9	3	1
9	8	1	3	4	2	5	6	7
7	6	3	8	1	5	2	4	9
2	4	5	6	9	7	3	1	8

89.

5	1	7	9	3	8	4	6	2
9	4	6	1	2	5	7	3	8
2	3	8	6	7	4	5	1	9
3	9	5	2	1	6	8	4	7
8	6	1	5	4	7	2	9	3
7	2	4	8	9	3	1	5	6
1	7	2	3	5	9	6	8	4
6	5	9	4	8	2	3	7	1
4	8	3	7	6	1	9	2	5

90.

9	1	4	5	6	7	3	2	8
5	2	6	3	1	8	4	7	9
8	3	7	2	9	4	1	5	6
4	6	1	8	2	9	5	3	7
2	7	9	6	5	3	8	4	1
3	5	8	4	7	1	9	6	2
1	9	5	7	4	6	2	8	3
6	8	2	1	3	5	7	9	4
7	4	3	9	8	2	6	1	5

91.

9	1	6	3	5	2	8	7	4
2	3	7	8	9	4	5	6	1
5	8	4	7	6	1	2	9	3
8	4	2	5	1	6	7	3	9
7	6	3	9	2	8	4	1	5
1	9	5	4	7	3	6	2	8
4	2	8	1	3	7	9	5	6
6	5	1	2	8	9	3	4	7
3	7	9	6	4	5	1	8	2

92.

3	7	5	8	4	6	2	9	1
4	8	2	9	1	7	5	6	3
9	6	1	3	5	2	8	4	7
7	2	6	4	3	5	1	8	9
5	1	9	6	2	8	3	7	4
8	4	3	1	7	9	6	5	2
6	5	4	2	9	1	7	3	8
2	9	8	7	6	3	4	1	5
1	3	7	5	8	4	9	2	6

93.

7	9	6	5	2	3	1	8	4
5	2	8	4	7	1	3	9	6
4	1	3	6	9	8	7	5	2
3	6	7	1	5	9	4	2	8
1	8	4	7	6	2	9	3	5
9	5	2	3	8	4	6	7	1
8	4	1	9	3	5	2	6	7
2	7	9	8	4	6	5	1	3
6	3	5	2	1	7	8	4	9

94.

6	3	2	8	7	4	5	9	1
4	8	1	6	9	5	3	2	7
9	7	5	2	3	1	4	8	6
2	9	3	4	6	8	7	1	5
8	5	6	9	1	7	2	3	4
7	1	4	3	5	2	8	6	9
3	2	7	1	4	6	9	5	8
5	6	9	7	8	3	1	4	2
1	4	8	5	2	9	6	7	3

95.

3	6	8	1	7	2	4	9	5
2	9	1	6	5	4	3	8	7
4	5	7	9	3	8	6	2	1
5	1	2	3	6	9	8	7	4
6	7	4	2	8	1	9	5	3
8	3	9	5	4	7	2	1	6
7	8	5	4	2	6	1	3	9
9	4	3	8	1	5	7	6	2
1	2	6	7	9	3	5	4	8

96.

8	4	9	5	2	1	3	6	7
3	2	7	8	4	6	5	9	1
6	1	5	3	9	7	2	8	4
1	3	6	2	8	9	4	7	5
5	8	4	6	7	3	1	2	9
7	9	2	4	1	5	8	3	6
4	5	3	7	6	2	9	1	8
2	7	1	9	5	8	6	4	3
9	6	8	1	3	4	7	5	2

97.

5	1	6	3	9	8	2	4	7
3	7	2	4	5	6	1	9	8
9	4	8	7	2	1	5	6	3
6	5	3	2	7	4	8	1	9
4	8	7	6	1	9	3	5	2
2	9	1	5	8	3	6	7	4
1	6	4	9	3	2	7	8	5
8	2	5	1	4	7	9	3	6
7	3	9	8	6	5	4	2	1

98.

7	1	3	6	9	2	5	4	8
5	8	9	3	7	4	6	2	1
2	6	4	8	1	5	3	7	9
1	3	6	9	4	8	2	5	7
4	2	5	7	6	1	9	8	3
8	9	7	2	5	3	4	1	6
3	7	2	5	8	6	1	9	4
9	5	1	4	3	7	8	6	2
6	4	8	1	2	9	7	3	5

99.

5	4	7	3	2	8	1	9	6
8	6	9	1	5	7	3	4	2
2	1	3	6	9	4	8	7	5
9	3	2	7	1	5	4	6	8
4	5	1	2	8	6	7	3	9
6	7	8	4	3	9	2	5	1
3	8	4	9	6	2	5	1	7
7	2	6	5	4	1	9	8	3
1	9	5	8	7	3	6	2	4

Solutions

100.

6	3	8	2	5	4	9	1	7
2	9	7	1	6	3	4	5	8
1	4	5	8	7	9	3	6	2
7	8	4	6	3	2	5	9	1
5	1	6	7	9	8	2	4	3
3	2	9	4	1	5	7	8	6
4	6	3	9	8	7	1	2	5
9	5	1	3	2	6	8	7	4
8	7	2	5	4	1	6	3	9

101.

4	9	1	8	2	7	6	5	3
5	2	7	3	6	1	8	4	9
6	8	3	5	9	4	7	2	1
8	7	5	2	3	9	4	1	6
1	6	4	7	5	8	3	9	2
9	3	2	4	1	6	5	7	8
2	5	8	9	4	3	1	6	7
7	1	9	6	8	5	2	3	4
3	4	6	1	7	2	9	8	5

102.

4	9	2	5	6	3	1	8	7
7	3	6	8	1	9	2	4	5
5	1	8	2	4	7	9	6	3
2	6	1	7	3	8	5	9	4
9	7	3	4	2	5	8	1	6
8	4	5	6	9	1	3	7	2
1	5	4	3	8	6	7	2	9
6	8	7	9	5	2	4	3	1
3	2	9	1	7	4	6	5	8

103.

7	2	5	8	6	3	1	9	4
8	3	4	1	9	2	5	7	6
9	1	6	7	4	5	8	3	2
2	7	8	6	3	9	4	5	1
5	4	3	2	7	1	6	8	9
6	9	1	4	5	8	7	2	3
4	5	9	3	8	6	2	1	7
3	6	2	5	1	7	9	4	8
1	8	7	9	2	4	3	6	5

104.

3	2	1	6	5	4	8	7	9
8	5	7	3	1	9	6	4	2
9	6	4	7	8	2	1	5	3
4	1	3	2	6	5	9	8	7
6	8	5	4	9	7	2	3	1
2	7	9	1	3	8	5	6	4
5	3	6	9	4	1	7	2	8
1	4	2	8	7	6	3	9	5
7	9	8	5	2	3	4	1	6

105.

6	5	9	8	1	4	2	3	7
1	3	4	2	7	6	8	5	9
8	7	2	9	3	5	4	6	1
4	2	5	7	9	3	1	8	6
7	8	6	5	2	1	9	4	3
9	1	3	6	4	8	7	2	5
5	4	8	1	6	9	3	7	2
2	6	1	3	8	7	5	9	4
3	9	7	4	5	2	6	1	8

106.

3	9	1	6	7	2	5	4	8
4	2	7	5	8	9	6	1	3
6	8	5	1	3	4	2	7	9
7	4	3	9	2	8	1	5	6
8	5	6	3	1	7	9	2	4
2	1	9	4	6	5	8	3	7
5	6	4	7	9	1	3	8	2
1	3	2	8	4	6	7	9	5
9	7	8	2	5	3	4	6	1

107.

3	4	6	2	8	1	7	9	5
9	2	8	7	5	3	1	6	4
5	7	1	9	6	4	8	2	3
4	9	2	5	1	6	3	8	7
6	8	3	4	7	9	2	5	1
7	1	5	3	2	8	9	4	6
1	6	7	8	9	5	4	3	2
2	3	9	6	4	7	5	1	8
8	5	4	1	3	2	6	7	9

108.

1	4	2	8	3	5	9	7	6
5	6	3	2	9	7	8	4	1
9	7	8	1	4	6	5	2	3
7	2	5	4	6	3	1	8	9
4	3	9	5	8	1	7	6	2
6	8	1	7	2	9	3	5	4
8	5	4	9	1	2	6	3	7
2	1	6	3	7	8	4	9	5
3	9	7	6	5	4	2	1	8

Solutions

109.

8	3	1	9	2	6	7	5	4
9	4	2	7	1	5	8	6	3
5	7	6	8	4	3	9	2	1
3	5	4	1	7	2	6	8	9
2	1	8	6	3	9	5	4	7
6	9	7	4	5	8	1	3	2
7	6	9	2	8	4	3	1	5
4	8	5	3	9	1	2	7	6
1	2	3	5	6	7	4	9	8

110.

3	9	8	4	2	7	1	5	6
2	6	1	3	8	5	9	4	7
4	5	7	9	6	1	8	2	3
1	4	3	5	7	8	6	9	2
8	7	5	2	9	6	4	3	1
6	2	9	1	4	3	5	7	8
9	8	6	7	3	4	2	1	5
7	1	4	6	5	2	3	8	9
5	3	2	8	1	9	7	6	4

111.

5	4	6	1	2	7	8	9	3
2	9	1	3	5	8	4	6	7
8	3	7	6	9	4	2	5	1
3	1	9	5	4	6	7	2	8
7	6	2	9	8	3	1	4	5
4	8	5	7	1	2	6	3	9
1	2	3	4	7	9	5	8	6
9	7	4	8	6	5	3	1	2
6	5	8	2	3	1	9	7	4

112.

4	5	7	9	1	2	6	8	3
1	6	8	5	7	3	4	9	2
3	2	9	6	4	8	5	7	1
9	1	6	4	3	5	7	2	8
2	8	4	7	6	1	9	3	5
7	3	5	8	2	9	1	6	4
5	9	2	1	8	6	3	4	7
8	4	1	3	9	7	2	5	6
6	7	3	2	5	4	8	1	9

113.

5	1	9	6	3	7	4	2	8
8	7	2	9	4	1	6	5	3
6	4	3	8	2	5	9	1	7
2	6	5	1	8	9	3	7	4
9	3	7	2	6	4	1	8	5
4	8	1	5	7	3	2	9	6
3	9	4	7	1	8	5	6	2
7	5	6	3	9	2	8	4	1
1	2	8	4	5	6	7	3	9

114.

5	1	3	6	2	7	9	8	4
7	8	2	5	9	4	6	1	3
4	9	6	1	3	8	2	5	7
9	6	5	7	1	3	4	2	8
1	3	4	9	8	2	5	7	6
8	2	7	4	5	6	3	9	1
2	4	9	8	6	1	7	3	5
3	7	8	2	4	5	1	6	9
6	5	1	3	7	9	8	4	2

115.

3	1	6	5	2	9	7	8	4
2	8	9	7	3	4	6	5	1
5	4	7	1	6	8	2	3	9
1	5	2	9	8	7	4	6	3
4	6	8	2	1	3	5	9	7
9	7	3	6	4	5	1	2	8
6	2	4	8	9	1	3	7	5
7	9	1	3	5	6	8	4	2
8	3	5	4	7	2	9	1	6

116.

6	5	3	4	7	1	8	9	2
2	9	4	3	5	8	7	6	1
8	7	1	9	6	2	5	3	4
3	4	9	7	1	6	2	8	5
5	1	2	8	4	3	9	7	6
7	8	6	5	2	9	1	4	3
1	3	7	6	9	5	4	2	8
4	6	5	2	8	7	3	1	9
9	2	8	1	3	4	6	5	7

117.

9	7	2	1	6	3	5	8	4
4	8	3	5	7	2	1	9	6
1	6	5	8	9	4	3	2	7
8	5	4	9	2	1	6	7	3
2	3	7	4	8	6	9	5	1
6	9	1	7	3	5	2	4	8
3	4	6	2	5	7	8	1	9
7	2	9	3	1	8	4	6	5
5	1	8	6	4	9	7	3	2

Solutions

118.

9	8	3	7	1	4	5	6	2
1	2	5	3	8	6	4	9	7
7	4	6	2	9	5	8	3	1
8	1	2	6	4	3	9	7	5
3	5	4	9	7	1	2	8	6
6	9	7	8	5	2	3	1	4
4	6	9	1	2	8	7	5	3
2	7	1	5	3	9	6	4	8
5	3	8	4	6	7	1	2	9

119.

8	5	6	3	7	4	2	1	9
3	9	1	2	8	6	4	5	7
7	2	4	5	9	1	3	6	8
4	7	3	6	1	9	5	8	2
1	6	2	8	4	5	9	7	3
9	8	5	7	2	3	1	4	6
6	4	9	1	3	7	8	2	5
5	1	8	9	6	2	7	3	4
2	3	7	4	5	8	6	9	1

120.

3	1	7	6	8	4	9	2	5
5	6	2	7	3	9	8	4	1
4	9	8	5	2	1	6	3	7
8	4	6	3	1	5	2	7	9
7	5	1	2	9	6	3	8	4
2	3	9	4	7	8	1	5	6
9	7	3	1	4	2	5	6	8
1	2	5	8	6	7	4	9	3
6	8	4	9	5	3	7	1	2

121.

5	1	7	3	9	4	8	2	6
8	4	6	2	7	1	3	9	5
2	3	9	5	8	6	4	1	7
7	8	1	4	2	5	6	3	9
3	9	5	6	1	8	7	4	2
6	2	4	9	3	7	5	8	1
1	6	2	7	4	3	9	5	8
9	5	3	8	6	2	1	7	4
4	7	8	1	5	9	2	6	3

122.

3	5	7	1	8	4	9	2	6
4	1	2	5	6	9	3	8	7
6	8	9	2	3	7	1	5	4
2	4	1	7	5	8	6	3	9
7	9	5	3	2	6	4	1	8
8	6	3	9	4	1	2	7	5
9	7	6	8	1	3	5	4	2
5	3	4	6	7	2	8	9	1
1	2	8	4	9	5	7	6	3

123.

4	1	9	6	8	2	3	7	5
3	6	2	4	7	5	8	9	1
8	5	7	1	9	3	4	2	6
2	3	1	5	6	8	9	4	7
5	4	8	9	3	7	6	1	2
9	7	6	2	4	1	5	3	8
6	2	5	3	1	9	7	8	4
1	8	3	7	5	4	2	6	9
7	9	4	8	2	6	1	5	3

124.

7	5	1	9	6	2	4	8	3
8	4	3	7	1	5	2	9	6
6	9	2	8	3	4	5	1	7
5	2	6	1	4	3	9	7	8
4	3	9	2	8	7	6	5	1
1	8	7	6	5	9	3	2	4
3	7	4	5	9	1	8	6	2
2	6	5	3	7	8	1	4	9
9	1	8	4	2	6	7	3	5

125.

5	2	6	9	7	1	8	4	3
4	8	3	2	5	6	9	7	1
7	9	1	8	4	3	5	2	6
9	5	2	3	6	7	1	8	4
6	3	4	1	9	8	7	5	2
1	7	8	4	2	5	6	3	9
2	4	5	7	1	9	3	6	8
8	6	9	5	3	2	4	1	7
3	1	7	6	8	4	2	9	5

126.

9	5	1	8	6	3	4	2	7
7	4	3	5	1	2	6	9	8
8	6	2	4	7	9	1	5	3
4	3	9	7	5	6	8	1	2
2	1	6	9	4	8	3	7	5
5	7	8	2	3	1	9	6	4
3	9	5	6	8	7	2	4	1
6	8	7	1	2	4	5	3	9
1	2	4	3	9	5	7	8	6

127.

3	4	9	8	6	5	2	7	1
5	7	8	1	9	2	3	6	4
2	6	1	7	4	3	5	9	8
7	1	3	4	2	6	8	5	9
4	2	5	9	7	8	1	3	6
8	9	6	3	5	1	4	2	7
1	3	7	5	8	9	6	4	2
9	8	2	6	3	4	7	1	5
6	5	4	2	1	7	9	8	3

128.

4	3	5	9	7	6	1	8	2
6	8	2	4	5	1	7	3	9
7	9	1	3	2	8	6	4	5
1	5	4	7	9	3	2	6	8
8	2	6	5	1	4	9	7	3
3	7	9	8	6	2	4	5	1
5	1	3	2	4	7	8	9	6
9	6	7	1	8	5	3	2	4
2	4	8	6	3	9	5	1	7

129.

9	1	7	4	3	2	5	8	6
5	6	4	9	1	8	3	7	2
3	8	2	7	6	5	4	9	1
2	9	6	5	7	4	8	1	3
4	5	1	6	8	3	7	2	9
8	7	3	2	9	1	6	5	4
6	4	5	1	2	7	9	3	8
1	3	9	8	5	6	2	4	7
7	2	8	3	4	9	1	6	5

130.

5	4	2	7	3	8	6	9	1
3	8	9	1	4	6	7	2	5
7	1	6	9	2	5	3	8	4
6	5	7	2	8	9	1	4	3
1	9	3	5	6	4	8	7	2
4	2	8	3	1	7	9	5	6
8	7	1	4	5	3	2	6	9
9	3	5	6	7	2	4	1	8
2	6	4	8	9	1	5	3	7

131.

3	6	5	2	7	4	1	9	8
8	4	2	9	5	1	7	3	6
1	9	7	8	6	3	4	5	2
7	5	3	4	2	6	8	1	9
9	8	6	7	1	5	3	2	4
2	1	4	3	9	8	5	6	7
6	3	9	5	8	7	2	4	1
5	7	1	6	4	2	9	8	3
4	2	8	1	3	9	6	7	5

132.

8	4	7	5	2	1	9	6	3
9	1	6	7	8	3	4	5	2
5	3	2	6	4	9	7	1	8
4	6	3	9	7	8	5	2	1
2	5	8	3	1	4	6	7	9
7	9	1	2	5	6	8	3	4
6	2	4	1	9	7	3	8	5
1	7	9	8	3	5	2	4	6
3	8	5	4	6	2	1	9	7

133.

1	7	9	3	2	4	5	6	8
5	4	8	7	6	9	2	3	1
3	6	2	8	1	5	7	4	9
6	1	4	9	5	3	8	7	2
2	9	3	6	7	8	1	5	4
8	5	7	1	4	2	6	9	3
7	2	1	4	9	6	3	8	5
4	8	6	5	3	1	9	2	7
9	3	5	2	8	7	4	1	6

134.

5	3	9	1	4	8	7	6	2
1	8	7	2	9	6	5	4	3
6	4	2	5	3	7	8	9	1
3	2	6	8	5	1	4	7	9
8	7	4	6	2	9	1	3	5
9	5	1	3	7	4	6	2	8
4	1	8	9	6	3	2	5	7
2	6	3	7	1	5	9	8	4
7	9	5	4	8	2	3	1	6

135.

5	4	1	9	3	2	6	7	8
2	9	7	5	8	6	4	1	3
6	8	3	4	1	7	9	2	5
4	6	5	3	7	9	2	8	1
3	2	9	1	4	8	7	5	6
7	1	8	2	6	5	3	9	4
8	3	4	7	2	1	5	6	9
9	7	6	8	5	4	1	3	2
1	5	2	6	9	3	8	4	7

Solutions

136.

```
6 9 8 1 3 2 7 5 4
5 3 4 7 8 6 9 2 1
7 1 2 4 9 5 8 6 3
8 7 1 6 5 3 4 9 2
4 6 9 2 7 8 3 1 5
2 5 3 9 1 4 6 7 8
3 2 6 5 4 9 1 8 7
1 4 5 8 6 7 2 3 9
9 8 7 3 2 1 5 4 6
```

137.

```
7 6 5 3 4 1 8 2 9
3 4 9 2 6 8 5 7 1
8 2 1 9 5 7 3 6 4
5 1 6 8 7 4 9 3 2
2 9 7 6 3 5 1 4 8
4 3 8 1 2 9 6 5 7
9 5 3 4 8 2 7 1 6
1 7 4 5 9 6 2 8 3
6 8 2 7 1 3 4 9 5
```

138.

```
3 5 8 1 4 2 9 6 7
7 9 1 6 3 5 2 4 8
6 2 4 7 9 8 5 1 3
2 8 9 4 5 7 1 3 6
1 4 6 9 2 3 7 8 5
5 3 7 8 6 1 4 2 9
4 6 3 2 7 9 8 5 1
8 7 2 5 1 6 3 9 4
9 1 5 3 8 4 6 7 2
```

139.

```
6 3 7 5 8 4 1 9 2
9 4 2 1 3 6 8 7 5
1 8 5 9 7 2 4 3 6
3 7 4 6 2 5 9 1 8
8 5 6 7 9 1 3 2 4
2 9 1 3 4 8 6 5 7
5 1 9 8 6 7 2 4 3
4 6 3 2 5 9 7 8 1
7 2 8 4 1 3 5 6 9
```

140.

```
3 1 9 7 6 4 2 8 5
2 4 6 1 8 5 9 3 7
5 8 7 2 9 3 4 6 1
9 6 2 5 3 7 8 1 4
7 5 1 8 4 6 3 2 9
4 3 8 9 1 2 5 7 6
8 7 4 6 2 9 1 5 3
6 2 3 4 5 1 7 9 8
1 9 5 3 7 8 6 4 2
```

141.

```
4 1 5 2 9 8 7 6 3
3 9 6 1 4 7 8 2 5
2 8 7 3 6 5 1 4 9
5 3 4 6 7 1 9 8 2
8 2 9 5 3 4 6 1 7
7 6 1 8 2 9 5 3 4
6 5 2 9 8 3 4 7 1
9 7 3 4 1 6 2 5 8
1 4 8 7 5 2 3 9 6
```

142.

```
8 2 9 5 4 7 3 6 1
5 7 4 6 1 3 9 2 8
3 6 1 9 8 2 5 4 7
6 4 8 7 3 5 1 9 2
2 9 3 1 6 8 7 5 4
7 1 5 4 2 9 8 3 6
1 3 2 8 5 4 6 7 9
9 5 6 2 7 1 4 8 3
4 8 7 3 9 6 2 1 5
```

143.

```
7 8 9 5 3 1 6 2 4
5 3 2 9 4 6 7 8 1
1 4 6 8 7 2 5 9 3
3 7 8 4 2 9 1 5 6
6 5 4 1 8 7 9 3 2
2 9 1 6 5 3 8 4 7
9 1 3 2 6 5 4 7 8
4 6 7 3 9 8 2 1 5
8 2 5 7 1 4 3 6 9
```

144.

```
6 8 9 3 4 5 7 1 2
2 4 3 7 1 8 9 5 6
7 1 5 6 9 2 3 8 4
3 9 8 1 2 4 6 7 5
5 2 4 9 6 7 8 3 1
1 7 6 5 8 3 4 2 9
8 5 1 4 7 6 2 9 3
4 3 2 8 5 9 1 6 7
9 6 7 2 3 1 5 4 8
```

Solutions

145.

2	6	5	4	7	1	9	8	3
8	4	7	9	5	3	1	6	2
1	3	9	6	2	8	4	5	7
4	7	3	5	8	2	6	1	9
6	9	2	1	4	7	8	3	5
5	1	8	3	9	6	2	7	4
9	8	1	2	3	5	7	4	6
7	5	4	8	6	9	3	2	1
3	2	6	7	1	4	5	9	8

146.

3	7	1	9	4	8	5	2	6
5	8	4	2	6	3	9	7	1
6	9	2	1	5	7	3	4	8
7	5	6	8	9	2	1	3	4
9	2	3	4	1	5	8	6	7
4	1	8	7	3	6	2	5	9
8	4	5	3	7	1	6	9	2
2	6	9	5	8	4	7	1	3
1	3	7	6	2	9	4	8	5

147.

1	2	3	9	7	6	5	4	8
8	4	5	1	2	3	6	7	9
6	7	9	8	5	4	3	1	2
5	1	8	6	3	2	4	9	7
7	6	2	4	9	8	1	3	5
9	3	4	7	1	5	8	2	6
3	8	6	2	4	9	7	5	1
4	9	7	5	6	1	2	8	3
2	5	1	3	8	7	9	6	4

148.

9	2	3	4	1	8	6	5	7
7	8	5	2	9	6	4	3	1
4	1	6	3	5	7	8	9	2
8	9	2	5	7	3	1	4	6
6	7	4	1	8	9	3	2	5
5	3	1	6	2	4	7	8	9
2	5	7	8	3	1	9	6	4
3	6	9	7	4	5	2	1	8
1	4	8	9	6	2	5	7	3

149.

1	7	9	4	5	8	3	6	2
2	8	4	3	6	7	9	5	1
6	5	3	1	9	2	4	7	8
3	2	7	8	1	6	5	9	4
8	4	6	5	7	9	2	1	3
9	1	5	2	4	3	7	8	6
7	3	2	9	8	1	6	4	5
5	9	1	6	2	4	8	3	7
4	6	8	7	3	5	1	2	9

150.

7	9	1	8	6	5	3	2	4
5	3	4	2	7	1	9	8	6
2	6	8	3	4	9	1	5	7
9	7	3	5	1	4	2	6	8
1	8	6	7	3	2	5	4	9
4	2	5	9	8	6	7	1	3
3	4	2	6	5	7	8	9	1
6	5	7	1	9	8	4	3	2
8	1	9	4	2	3	6	7	5

151.

7	2	4	9	1	8	3	5	6
1	3	5	6	7	2	4	9	8
6	9	8	4	3	5	7	1	2
8	5	3	7	4	9	2	6	1
4	7	6	2	5	1	8	3	9
9	1	2	3	8	6	5	7	4
3	8	1	5	6	4	9	2	7
2	4	7	1	9	3	6	8	5
5	6	9	8	2	7	1	4	3

152.

6	2	9	8	1	5	3	7	4
1	8	3	2	7	4	5	6	9
7	5	4	6	9	3	8	1	2
3	9	5	1	4	2	7	8	6
4	7	8	5	3	6	9	2	1
2	6	1	7	8	9	4	5	3
8	4	2	9	5	1	6	3	7
9	1	7	3	6	8	2	4	5
5	3	6	4	2	7	1	9	8

153.

7	2	9	8	5	4	1	6	3
4	5	6	3	7	1	2	8	9
3	8	1	2	6	9	7	4	5
1	4	2	7	9	8	3	5	6
5	9	7	1	3	6	8	2	4
6	3	8	5	4	2	9	1	7
9	1	3	4	2	5	6	7	8
2	6	4	9	8	7	5	3	1
8	7	5	6	1	3	4	9	2

Solutions

154.

2	4	5	3	8	9	1	6	7
3	7	9	1	5	6	8	4	2
8	1	6	7	4	2	3	5	9
5	6	1	2	9	4	7	3	8
7	9	2	8	6	3	4	1	5
4	3	8	5	7	1	2	9	6
1	5	7	6	3	8	9	2	4
9	8	3	4	2	5	6	7	1
6	2	4	9	1	7	5	8	3

155.

8	9	2	7	4	5	3	1	6
7	4	6	9	1	3	8	5	2
1	3	5	2	8	6	7	9	4
2	7	3	6	5	4	1	8	9
9	1	8	3	7	2	6	4	5
5	6	4	8	9	1	2	3	7
4	2	1	5	6	8	9	7	3
6	8	7	4	3	9	5	2	1
3	5	9	1	2	7	4	6	8

156.

9	2	8	4	7	3	5	6	1
6	3	1	8	9	5	7	2	4
5	7	4	1	2	6	3	9	8
3	9	2	5	8	1	6	4	7
4	8	5	7	6	9	2	1	3
7	1	6	3	4	2	9	8	5
2	5	3	9	1	8	4	7	6
1	4	9	6	3	7	8	5	2
8	6	7	2	5	4	1	3	9

157.

1	8	6	2	5	3	9	7	4
7	2	3	9	4	8	6	1	5
4	9	5	7	6	1	3	8	2
8	7	1	3	9	2	5	4	6
3	5	4	6	1	7	8	2	9
9	6	2	4	8	5	1	3	7
6	3	9	1	2	4	7	5	8
5	4	7	8	3	9	2	6	1
2	1	8	5	7	6	4	9	3

158.

9	8	2	6	3	7	1	5	4
4	1	3	5	8	2	9	7	6
6	7	5	4	9	1	8	3	2
7	6	4	2	1	8	3	9	5
5	2	8	9	6	3	4	1	7
3	9	1	7	4	5	2	6	8
2	3	9	8	5	6	7	4	1
1	5	7	3	2	4	6	8	9
8	4	6	1	7	9	5	2	3

159.

2	7	5	6	9	1	3	4	8
3	4	6	2	7	8	5	9	1
1	8	9	5	3	4	6	2	7
9	1	3	8	4	5	2	7	6
7	5	2	9	1	6	8	3	4
4	6	8	3	2	7	9	1	5
5	2	4	7	6	3	1	8	9
6	9	1	4	8	2	7	5	3
8	3	7	1	5	9	4	6	2

160.

7	9	1	3	2	8	6	4	5
4	5	2	1	6	7	9	3	8
3	6	8	5	4	9	2	7	1
6	8	9	2	7	3	1	5	4
1	7	5	9	8	4	3	2	6
2	3	4	6	5	1	8	9	7
5	2	3	4	1	6	7	8	9
9	1	7	8	3	5	4	6	2
8	4	6	7	9	2	5	1	3

161.

1	8	2	4	3	9	5	6	7
5	4	6	2	1	7	3	8	9
3	7	9	6	5	8	4	2	1
2	1	7	9	8	3	6	5	4
4	9	5	7	2	6	1	3	8
6	3	8	5	4	1	7	9	2
9	6	4	8	7	5	2	1	3
7	5	1	3	9	2	8	4	6
8	2	3	1	6	4	9	7	5

162.

8	5	4	9	7	3	6	2	1
6	9	1	2	8	4	5	3	7
7	3	2	5	1	6	8	9	4
5	1	6	7	9	8	2	4	3
9	4	8	6	3	2	1	7	5
3	2	7	1	4	5	9	6	8
2	7	3	8	5	9	4	1	6
1	8	9	4	6	7	3	5	2
4	6	5	3	2	1	7	8	9

Solutions

163.

8	1	9	3	2	5	6	7	4
4	6	2	9	7	8	5	1	3
5	7	3	1	6	4	9	8	2
3	8	1	6	9	2	7	4	5
6	2	4	7	5	3	8	9	1
9	5	7	8	4	1	2	3	6
7	4	6	2	1	9	3	5	8
2	3	5	4	8	7	1	6	9
1	9	8	5	3	6	4	2	7

164.

5	9	1	7	2	8	4	3	6
4	7	3	5	1	6	8	2	9
2	8	6	9	3	4	5	7	1
6	4	5	2	8	7	9	1	3
7	3	9	1	4	5	6	8	2
1	2	8	3	6	9	7	4	5
3	6	7	8	5	1	2	9	4
8	1	4	6	9	2	3	5	7
9	5	2	4	7	3	1	6	8

165.

2	6	4	5	9	1	3	7	8
5	8	1	3	4	7	6	9	2
9	3	7	8	2	6	4	1	5
8	9	6	2	5	3	7	4	1
1	4	5	9	7	8	2	6	3
3	7	2	1	6	4	5	8	9
7	1	9	6	3	5	8	2	4
4	5	8	7	1	2	9	3	6
6	2	3	4	8	9	1	5	7

166.

9	6	5	4	1	3	7	2	8
4	1	7	9	8	2	6	5	3
3	2	8	7	5	6	1	9	4
5	7	4	6	3	9	8	1	2
1	3	2	5	7	8	9	4	6
8	9	6	1	2	4	5	3	7
2	4	1	8	6	5	3	7	9
7	8	3	2	9	1	4	6	5
6	5	9	3	4	7	2	8	1

167.

1	8	9	6	2	4	7	5	3
4	2	5	1	3	7	9	8	6
7	6	3	5	8	9	4	1	2
8	9	2	4	1	5	6	3	7
6	3	1	8	7	2	5	4	9
5	4	7	9	6	3	8	2	1
3	7	6	2	5	8	1	9	4
9	1	8	3	4	6	2	7	5
2	5	4	7	9	1	3	6	8

168.

8	9	4	7	1	5	6	2	3
3	1	6	4	8	2	5	7	9
5	2	7	3	6	9	4	1	8
7	5	1	9	4	3	8	6	2
6	8	9	2	7	1	3	4	5
4	3	2	6	5	8	7	9	1
2	6	8	1	3	7	9	5	4
1	7	3	5	9	4	2	8	6
9	4	5	8	2	6	1	3	7

169.

7	3	1	9	6	4	5	2	8
6	8	5	1	2	3	7	9	4
2	9	4	5	7	8	1	3	6
9	2	3	4	8	7	6	5	1
4	1	6	2	3	5	9	8	7
5	7	8	6	1	9	2	4	3
3	6	7	8	5	2	4	1	9
8	4	2	7	9	1	3	6	5
1	5	9	3	4	6	8	7	2

170.

1	6	3	4	7	2	8	9	5
2	8	4	6	9	5	7	3	1
9	5	7	1	3	8	6	4	2
4	3	9	7	2	1	5	8	6
7	2	6	8	5	4	3	1	9
5	1	8	9	6	3	2	7	4
8	9	2	5	4	7	1	6	3
3	4	1	2	8	6	9	5	7
6	7	5	3	1	9	4	2	8

171.

5	6	1	3	9	4	8	2	7
8	2	7	5	6	1	3	4	9
9	3	4	8	7	2	5	6	1
1	8	9	4	5	7	6	3	2
2	5	6	9	1	3	7	8	4
4	7	3	2	8	6	1	9	5
7	4	2	6	3	5	9	1	8
6	1	8	7	2	9	4	5	3
3	9	5	1	4	8	2	7	6

Solutions

172.

5	1	7	2	8	3	6	9	4
3	6	4	1	9	7	8	5	2
2	8	9	4	6	5	7	1	3
9	4	3	8	5	6	1	2	7
1	7	2	3	4	9	5	6	8
8	5	6	7	2	1	4	3	9
6	9	8	5	7	2	3	4	1
7	2	1	6	3	4	9	8	5
4	3	5	9	1	8	2	7	6

173.

8	7	9	2	5	1	3	4	6
5	3	4	9	8	6	1	7	2
6	1	2	3	7	4	9	5	8
1	8	5	6	4	9	7	2	3
2	4	3	7	1	8	6	9	5
9	6	7	5	3	2	4	8	1
7	2	8	1	9	3	5	6	4
3	5	6	4	2	7	8	1	9
4	9	1	8	6	5	2	3	7

174.

3	9	5	1	7	6	8	2	4
4	7	6	9	8	2	5	3	1
2	8	1	5	4	3	9	6	7
5	2	7	3	1	4	6	9	8
9	3	4	7	6	8	2	1	5
6	1	8	2	5	9	7	4	3
7	5	2	4	9	1	3	8	6
1	6	3	8	2	7	4	5	9
8	4	9	6	3	5	1	7	2

175.

9	5	2	3	7	8	4	1	6
1	4	8	6	9	2	5	7	3
3	6	7	1	4	5	9	8	2
7	3	5	4	1	9	2	6	8
8	1	6	5	2	3	7	4	9
2	9	4	8	6	7	3	5	1
5	2	9	7	8	6	1	3	4
6	7	1	9	3	4	8	2	5
4	8	3	2	5	1	6	9	7

176.

8	7	1	9	4	2	5	3	6
2	9	4	6	3	5	7	1	8
6	3	5	1	7	8	2	4	9
9	6	7	5	1	4	8	2	3
5	2	8	3	9	7	4	6	1
1	4	3	8	2	6	9	5	7
7	5	6	2	8	3	1	9	4
3	8	9	4	5	1	6	7	2
4	1	2	7	6	9	3	8	5

177.

8	3	6	4	1	5	9	7	2
1	5	4	7	2	9	6	8	3
2	9	7	3	8	6	1	5	4
7	1	3	2	4	8	5	9	6
5	8	2	9	6	7	4	3	1
6	4	9	5	3	1	7	2	8
3	7	8	1	9	4	2	6	5
9	6	1	8	5	2	3	4	7
4	2	5	6	7	3	8	1	9

178.

1	6	4	2	7	9	3	5	8
7	2	8	3	5	6	9	1	4
3	5	9	1	8	4	6	2	7
2	9	1	6	3	7	8	4	5
6	4	3	5	1	8	2	7	9
8	7	5	9	4	2	1	6	3
5	8	2	7	9	1	4	3	6
9	1	7	4	6	3	5	8	2
4	3	6	8	2	5	7	9	1

179.

3	9	4	5	7	1	8	6	2
1	2	5	9	8	6	3	7	4
7	8	6	4	3	2	5	9	1
9	1	8	3	6	7	2	4	5
6	5	7	2	4	8	9	1	3
2	4	3	1	5	9	7	8	6
4	6	2	7	9	5	1	3	8
8	7	1	6	2	3	4	5	9
5	3	9	8	1	4	6	2	7

180.

1	6	5	3	4	2	7	9	8
9	3	7	1	8	5	6	4	2
2	4	8	9	6	7	5	1	3
7	5	4	2	1	6	3	8	9
3	2	6	7	9	8	4	5	1
8	9	1	5	3	4	2	7	6
4	7	3	8	2	1	9	6	5
6	1	9	4	5	3	8	2	7
5	8	2	6	7	9	1	3	4

181.

6	8	1	3	2	9	5	4	7
2	5	7	4	1	6	8	9	3
9	4	3	5	7	8	2	6	1
3	6	5	9	4	1	7	8	2
1	2	4	8	6	7	3	5	9
8	7	9	2	5	3	4	1	6
4	1	6	7	3	5	9	2	8
5	3	8	6	9	2	1	7	4
7	9	2	1	8	4	6	3	5

182.

1	9	3	4	6	2	5	8	7
5	7	8	9	3	1	6	4	2
4	2	6	7	8	5	9	3	1
7	3	1	8	5	4	2	9	6
9	6	5	3	2	7	4	1	8
2	8	4	6	1	9	3	7	5
8	4	9	2	7	6	1	5	3
6	1	7	5	9	3	8	2	4
3	5	2	1	4	8	7	6	9

183.

4	9	6	7	5	8	3	1	2
3	5	7	1	9	2	8	4	6
8	1	2	4	6	3	5	7	9
6	2	3	5	1	9	7	8	4
1	7	5	8	2	4	9	6	3
9	8	4	3	7	6	1	2	5
7	4	9	6	8	5	2	3	1
5	6	1	2	3	7	4	9	8
2	3	8	9	4	1	6	5	7

184.

1	8	2	4	5	3	6	9	7
4	3	6	7	9	1	8	2	5
5	7	9	6	2	8	4	3	1
7	9	4	8	3	6	1	5	2
3	1	5	2	4	9	7	8	6
6	2	8	1	7	5	9	4	3
9	5	7	3	6	4	2	1	8
8	6	3	9	1	2	5	7	4
2	4	1	5	8	7	3	6	9

185.

1	2	6	8	5	7	9	4	3
7	8	3	6	9	4	2	1	5
5	9	4	2	3	1	7	8	6
9	3	1	5	4	8	6	7	2
6	5	2	1	7	9	4	3	8
4	7	8	3	2	6	1	5	9
8	6	9	7	1	3	5	2	4
3	1	5	4	6	2	8	9	7
2	4	7	9	8	5	3	6	1

186.

2	8	1	7	3	4	6	9	5
4	6	7	5	2	9	1	3	8
3	9	5	6	1	8	4	7	2
8	5	4	9	6	2	7	1	3
9	7	2	1	8	3	5	4	6
6	1	3	4	5	7	8	2	9
1	3	8	2	7	6	9	5	4
7	2	9	8	4	5	3	6	1
5	4	6	3	9	1	2	8	7

187.

8	5	7	9	6	1	2	4	3
3	1	2	4	8	7	9	5	6
9	4	6	5	3	2	7	8	1
7	2	9	1	4	5	6	3	8
6	3	4	7	2	8	5	1	9
1	8	5	3	9	6	4	7	2
5	9	3	2	1	4	8	6	7
2	7	8	6	5	3	1	9	4
4	6	1	8	7	9	3	2	5

188.

1	9	7	8	3	4	5	6	2
3	5	8	1	6	2	7	9	4
6	4	2	9	7	5	3	1	8
9	7	1	4	5	8	2	3	6
5	3	4	7	2	6	9	8	1
2	8	6	3	1	9	4	7	5
4	1	3	5	8	7	6	2	9
8	6	5	2	9	3	1	4	7
7	2	9	6	4	1	8	5	3

189.

6	9	7	5	3	4	8	1	2
1	4	8	9	2	6	5	3	7
5	3	2	7	8	1	6	4	9
2	5	9	8	4	7	3	6	1
3	1	4	2	6	5	7	9	8
8	7	6	1	9	3	2	5	4
7	8	3	4	5	9	1	2	6
4	2	5	6	1	8	9	7	3
9	6	1	3	7	2	4	8	5

Solutions

190.

8	3	7	4	1	6	9	2	5
4	5	2	7	9	8	3	6	1
9	6	1	2	3	5	7	4	8
7	4	9	1	6	2	8	5	3
3	2	5	8	4	9	1	7	6
6	1	8	3	5	7	2	9	4
2	7	3	6	8	4	5	1	9
1	9	6	5	2	3	4	8	7
5	8	4	9	7	1	6	3	2

191.

5	1	2	6	7	4	9	8	3
4	3	8	5	9	1	7	6	2
9	6	7	2	8	3	5	4	1
8	9	6	1	5	2	4	3	7
1	7	5	4	3	8	2	9	6
3	2	4	7	6	9	8	1	5
6	8	9	3	2	7	1	5	4
2	4	3	8	1	5	6	7	9
7	5	1	9	4	6	3	2	8

192.

9	3	8	1	4	6	5	7	2
6	5	7	3	2	9	4	1	8
4	2	1	7	8	5	9	3	6
3	1	5	6	9	4	2	8	7
8	4	6	5	7	2	3	9	1
2	7	9	8	3	1	6	4	5
1	9	2	4	6	8	7	5	3
7	8	4	2	5	3	1	6	9
5	6	3	9	1	7	8	2	4

193.

2	5	6	9	3	4	7	8	1
9	3	8	7	1	6	2	5	4
1	7	4	8	5	2	3	6	9
7	4	5	3	9	1	8	2	6
3	8	2	4	6	7	9	1	5
6	9	1	2	8	5	4	7	3
8	6	3	1	2	9	5	4	7
5	2	7	6	4	3	1	9	8
4	1	9	5	7	8	6	3	2

194.

5	4	9	8	2	1	7	6	3
1	6	7	3	9	4	2	5	8
3	2	8	7	6	5	9	4	1
6	8	4	2	5	7	3	1	9
9	7	5	6	1	3	4	8	2
2	1	3	4	8	9	5	7	6
4	3	2	1	7	6	8	9	5
8	5	6	9	4	2	1	3	7
7	9	1	5	3	8	6	2	4

195.

1	9	6	4	5	8	2	7	3
3	7	4	2	9	1	8	5	6
5	2	8	7	3	6	1	4	9
7	3	5	9	8	2	4	6	1
8	6	1	5	7	4	9	3	2
2	4	9	1	6	3	5	8	7
4	5	7	3	1	9	6	2	8
6	1	2	8	4	7	3	9	5
9	8	3	6	2	5	7	1	4

196.

3	4	5	6	9	7	8	1	2
9	8	1	2	4	5	3	7	6
6	2	7	3	8	1	4	5	9
7	3	4	1	6	2	5	9	8
2	9	8	5	3	4	1	6	7
5	1	6	9	7	8	2	3	4
4	5	3	7	2	9	6	8	1
8	6	9	4	1	3	7	2	5
1	7	2	8	5	6	9	4	3

197.

8	7	6	4	5	9	1	3	2
2	9	3	8	6	1	7	5	4
4	1	5	2	7	3	6	8	9
3	8	4	1	2	7	9	6	5
6	5	7	3	9	4	2	1	8
9	2	1	6	8	5	3	4	7
1	6	9	7	4	8	5	2	3
5	4	2	9	3	6	8	7	1
7	3	8	5	1	2	4	9	6

198.

7	1	2	3	4	8	6	9	5
9	3	4	5	7	6	2	1	8
8	5	6	2	1	9	4	3	7
4	8	7	9	5	1	3	6	2
6	9	5	4	2	3	8	7	1
1	2	3	6	8	7	5	4	9
3	6	8	1	9	5	7	2	4
2	7	9	8	3	4	1	5	6
5	4	1	7	6	2	9	8	3

199.

6	8	3	4	9	5	1	2	7
7	1	2	8	6	3	4	5	9
9	4	5	2	7	1	6	3	8
1	6	8	3	2	4	9	7	5
3	9	4	6	5	7	2	8	1
5	2	7	1	8	9	3	4	6
4	5	6	7	1	2	8	9	3
8	3	9	5	4	6	7	1	2
2	7	1	9	3	8	5	6	4

200.

2	4	6	1	7	5	3	8	9
7	3	8	4	9	6	2	1	5
1	9	5	3	8	2	4	7	6
4	8	2	7	5	3	6	9	1
6	7	3	9	1	4	5	2	8
5	1	9	2	6	8	7	4	3
9	6	7	5	4	1	8	3	2
3	5	4	8	2	9	1	6	7
8	2	1	6	3	7	9	5	4

201.

1	6	8	2	4	7	9	3	5
2	4	3	6	9	5	7	1	8
5	9	7	8	1	3	6	2	4
3	5	2	9	6	8	1	4	7
4	1	9	5	7	2	3	8	6
7	8	6	1	3	4	5	9	2
6	7	4	3	8	1	2	5	9
8	3	5	7	2	9	4	6	1
9	2	1	4	5	6	8	7	3

202.

5	3	2	4	8	7	9	1	6
8	9	4	6	1	5	7	2	3
7	1	6	2	9	3	5	4	8
9	7	3	5	2	4	6	8	1
2	4	5	8	6	1	3	7	9
1	6	8	3	7	9	4	5	2
6	2	7	9	5	8	1	3	4
3	8	1	7	4	6	2	9	5
4	5	9	1	3	2	8	6	7

203.

5	3	1	9	8	2	4	7	6
7	8	4	6	3	5	2	1	9
2	6	9	4	7	1	5	8	3
4	7	3	1	5	8	9	6	2
9	2	8	3	6	4	1	5	7
1	5	6	7	2	9	8	3	4
3	1	2	8	9	6	7	4	5
6	4	5	2	1	7	3	9	8
8	9	7	5	4	3	6	2	1

204.

8	3	9	6	2	4	1	5	7
5	4	6	8	1	7	2	9	3
7	2	1	9	5	3	6	4	8
4	7	5	1	8	9	3	6	2
1	8	2	3	4	6	9	7	5
6	9	3	2	7	5	4	8	1
2	5	7	4	6	1	8	3	9
9	1	4	5	3	8	7	2	6
3	6	8	7	9	2	5	1	4

205.

6	9	5	8	7	4	2	3	1
7	8	2	1	3	6	5	9	4
4	3	1	9	5	2	6	7	8
2	4	6	7	8	1	3	5	9
5	1	8	2	9	3	7	4	6
3	7	9	4	6	5	8	1	2
1	6	4	5	2	7	9	8	3
9	2	7	3	4	8	1	6	5
8	5	3	6	1	9	4	2	7

206.

7	9	2	1	8	4	3	6	5
6	4	3	2	5	9	7	1	8
5	1	8	6	3	7	4	9	2
9	3	4	8	1	2	5	7	6
2	5	1	4	7	6	8	3	9
8	7	6	5	9	3	1	2	4
4	2	5	3	6	1	9	8	7
1	6	7	9	4	8	2	5	3
3	8	9	7	2	5	6	4	1

207.

4	7	6	5	2	1	9	8	3
3	5	2	8	4	9	7	6	1
1	8	9	6	7	3	4	5	2
8	4	7	1	6	2	5	3	9
2	9	3	4	5	8	6	1	7
5	6	1	3	9	7	8	2	4
7	2	8	9	3	5	1	4	6
6	3	5	7	1	4	2	9	8
9	1	4	2	8	6	3	7	5

Solutions

208.

4	9	6	8	5	3	2	7	1
1	5	7	6	9	2	8	3	4
2	3	8	1	7	4	9	6	5
3	1	9	4	8	5	7	2	6
8	7	5	2	6	9	4	1	3
6	2	4	3	1	7	5	8	9
5	4	1	7	3	8	6	9	2
7	6	2	9	4	1	3	5	8
9	8	3	5	2	6	1	4	7

209.

8	1	9	5	3	4	2	6	7
5	3	2	7	6	8	1	4	9
4	7	6	9	1	2	8	5	3
9	6	1	3	8	5	7	2	4
7	4	3	1	2	6	5	9	8
2	5	8	4	9	7	3	1	6
1	9	5	8	4	3	6	7	2
6	8	4	2	7	1	9	3	5
3	2	7	6	5	9	4	8	1

210.

7	9	6	4	8	5	2	3	1
4	8	2	6	1	3	9	7	5
5	3	1	7	9	2	8	6	4
3	6	4	8	7	9	5	1	2
9	1	7	5	2	6	3	4	8
8	2	5	1	3	4	6	9	7
1	4	3	2	6	8	7	5	9
6	7	8	9	5	1	4	2	3
2	5	9	3	4	7	1	8	6

211.

9	1	5	8	7	4	6	3	2
6	2	4	3	1	5	7	9	8
7	3	8	9	2	6	5	1	4
5	6	1	7	4	9	2	8	3
3	4	2	1	6	8	9	7	5
8	7	9	2	5	3	1	4	6
2	9	6	4	8	7	3	5	1
4	5	3	6	9	1	8	2	7
1	8	7	5	3	2	4	6	9

212.

1	2	5	6	7	9	3	4	8
4	3	9	5	1	8	2	6	7
7	6	8	4	3	2	1	5	9
3	1	6	9	5	7	4	8	2
9	8	4	1	2	3	6	7	5
2	5	7	8	6	4	9	1	3
8	4	3	7	9	1	5	2	6
5	9	1	2	8	6	7	3	4
6	7	2	3	4	5	8	9	1

213.

2	8	1	5	9	3	4	6	7
6	3	5	1	7	4	9	2	8
7	4	9	8	2	6	5	3	1
9	1	6	2	5	7	8	4	3
8	2	4	3	1	9	7	5	6
5	7	3	4	6	8	1	9	2
1	6	8	9	3	5	2	7	4
3	9	2	7	4	1	6	8	5
4	5	7	6	8	2	3	1	9

214.

5	6	2	7	8	1	9	4	3
7	9	3	6	2	4	1	5	8
1	8	4	3	9	5	7	2	6
9	5	1	4	6	3	2	8	7
2	3	6	1	7	8	4	9	5
4	7	8	2	5	9	3	6	1
8	1	9	5	3	2	6	7	4
3	2	7	8	4	6	5	1	9
6	4	5	9	1	7	8	3	2

215.

8	7	6	1	9	3	2	4	5
5	2	9	8	4	7	3	1	6
1	4	3	2	6	5	7	8	9
2	6	1	9	5	4	8	3	7
9	3	7	6	8	2	4	5	1
4	5	8	7	3	1	9	6	2
6	8	4	5	2	9	1	7	3
7	9	5	3	1	8	6	2	4
3	1	2	4	7	6	5	9	8

216.

2	8	7	5	6	3	4	9	1
3	9	5	1	4	7	6	8	2
6	1	4	2	9	8	7	3	5
8	7	6	3	5	9	1	2	4
9	3	1	6	2	4	8	5	7
4	5	2	7	8	1	9	6	3
7	6	3	8	1	5	2	4	9
1	4	8	9	3	2	5	7	6
5	2	9	4	7	6	3	1	8

Solutions

217.

1	4	8	6	5	7	3	9	2
2	9	6	4	3	8	7	1	5
7	5	3	1	2	9	8	6	4
5	3	2	9	7	1	4	8	6
4	6	9	3	8	5	2	7	1
8	1	7	2	4	6	5	3	9
9	8	5	7	1	2	6	4	3
6	7	4	5	9	3	1	2	8
3	2	1	8	6	4	9	5	7

218.

7	8	3	4	1	5	6	2	9
4	5	9	2	8	6	7	1	3
1	6	2	9	3	7	4	5	8
8	9	1	7	2	3	5	6	4
5	4	6	8	9	1	2	3	7
2	3	7	5	6	4	9	8	1
6	7	8	3	4	2	1	9	5
9	2	5	1	7	8	3	4	6
3	1	4	6	5	9	8	7	2

219.

2	3	4	9	6	5	7	1	8
6	1	8	4	3	7	9	5	2
9	5	7	8	2	1	6	4	3
1	8	9	6	5	2	4	3	7
3	4	6	7	1	8	5	2	9
5	7	2	3	4	9	1	8	6
4	9	5	2	8	6	3	7	1
8	6	1	5	7	3	2	9	4
7	2	3	1	9	4	8	6	5

220.

2	8	5	7	9	4	3	6	1
6	7	3	5	1	8	9	4	2
4	9	1	6	3	2	7	8	5
9	4	2	1	5	7	8	3	6
1	6	8	4	2	3	5	7	9
5	3	7	9	8	6	1	2	4
8	5	4	3	6	1	2	9	7
3	1	6	2	7	9	4	5	8
7	2	9	8	4	5	6	1	3

221.

5	4	2	3	1	8	7	6	9
6	8	7	9	5	2	1	4	3
1	9	3	4	6	7	8	2	5
3	5	8	2	7	1	6	9	4
9	7	6	8	4	5	3	1	2
4	2	1	6	3	9	5	8	7
7	3	9	1	2	6	4	5	8
2	1	5	7	8	4	9	3	6
8	6	4	5	9	3	2	7	1

222.

3	6	2	9	5	4	1	7	8
4	7	5	8	1	3	6	2	9
9	1	8	6	2	7	4	5	3
7	5	9	4	8	2	3	6	1
6	4	3	1	7	9	2	8	5
2	8	1	5	3	6	9	4	7
5	2	6	3	9	8	7	1	4
8	9	7	2	4	1	5	3	6
1	3	4	7	6	5	8	9	2

223.

4	7	2	8	6	9	3	1	5
9	5	3	7	4	1	2	8	6
6	8	1	2	5	3	7	9	4
5	1	7	6	2	4	9	3	8
8	3	9	5	1	7	6	4	2
2	4	6	9	3	8	5	7	1
7	6	8	4	9	5	1	2	3
1	2	4	3	7	6	8	5	9
3	9	5	1	8	2	4	6	7

224.

1	5	2	4	6	7	8	9	3
7	6	8	3	5	9	2	1	4
9	3	4	1	2	8	7	5	6
4	8	1	7	9	3	6	2	5
6	7	5	8	4	2	1	3	9
2	9	3	5	1	6	4	8	7
8	4	9	2	7	5	3	6	1
3	1	6	9	8	4	5	7	2
5	2	7	6	3	1	9	4	8

225.

8	5	4	1	9	7	3	2	6
2	9	3	5	6	8	1	4	7
1	7	6	2	3	4	5	9	8
4	2	7	3	5	9	8	6	1
9	3	1	8	4	6	7	5	2
5	6	8	7	2	1	9	3	4
6	8	5	9	7	2	4	1	3
7	4	9	6	1	3	2	8	5
3	1	2	4	8	5	6	7	9

Solutions

226.

3	8	6	1	9	7	4	5	2
4	1	2	8	6	5	3	7	9
5	9	7	3	4	2	1	8	6
8	7	1	2	3	6	5	9	4
9	2	4	7	5	8	6	1	3
6	5	3	4	1	9	8	2	7
7	4	8	6	2	1	9	3	5
2	6	9	5	8	3	7	4	1
1	3	5	9	7	4	2	6	8

227.

6	8	7	5	2	4	3	1	9
2	1	3	9	7	6	4	5	8
4	5	9	1	8	3	7	2	6
8	3	5	2	4	7	6	9	1
7	2	6	8	9	1	5	4	3
1	9	4	3	6	5	8	7	2
9	6	2	4	5	8	1	3	7
3	4	8	7	1	9	2	6	5
5	7	1	6	3	2	9	8	4

228.

8	1	6	9	5	4	2	3	7
2	3	9	1	6	7	5	4	8
7	5	4	2	3	8	9	1	6
6	9	1	4	2	3	8	7	5
3	8	2	6	7	5	1	9	4
4	7	5	8	9	1	3	6	2
1	2	3	7	8	6	4	5	9
5	6	8	3	4	9	7	2	1
9	4	7	5	1	2	6	8	3

229.

5	4	8	2	1	9	3	6	7
7	6	1	4	5	3	2	9	8
9	2	3	6	7	8	5	1	4
1	3	5	8	2	6	4	7	9
8	9	2	7	4	1	6	3	5
4	7	6	3	9	5	8	2	1
3	1	4	9	8	2	7	5	6
6	5	7	1	3	4	9	8	2
2	8	9	5	6	7	1	4	3

230.

9	8	6	5	7	1	3	2	4
7	1	4	8	2	3	5	9	6
5	3	2	9	4	6	1	7	8
4	2	8	3	1	9	6	5	7
6	5	9	7	8	2	4	3	1
3	7	1	4	6	5	2	8	9
2	4	7	6	3	8	9	1	5
8	9	3	1	5	4	7	6	2
1	6	5	2	9	7	8	4	3

231.

1	8	5	9	7	6	4	3	2
4	7	9	5	2	3	6	1	8
2	3	6	8	1	4	5	9	7
6	4	2	7	5	1	9	8	3
5	1	3	4	8	9	2	7	6
7	9	8	6	3	2	1	4	5
8	6	7	1	4	5	3	2	9
9	2	4	3	6	7	8	5	1
3	5	1	2	9	8	7	6	4

232.

3	8	2	5	6	4	1	7	9
5	1	6	9	2	7	8	3	4
9	4	7	3	1	8	6	5	2
6	9	4	7	8	1	3	2	5
7	2	5	6	3	9	4	1	8
8	3	1	4	5	2	9	6	7
1	7	3	8	9	5	2	4	6
4	6	8	2	7	3	5	9	1
2	5	9	1	4	6	7	8	3

233.

7	6	4	5	2	9	1	3	8
1	5	9	8	3	7	6	2	4
2	8	3	1	4	6	5	9	7
5	7	2	4	6	8	9	1	3
8	4	6	3	9	1	2	7	5
3	9	1	2	7	5	4	8	6
4	3	5	7	1	2	8	6	9
9	1	8	6	5	3	7	4	2
6	2	7	9	8	4	3	5	1

234.

5	6	2	3	1	8	7	9	4
1	8	3	4	7	9	5	6	2
4	9	7	2	6	5	8	3	1
9	2	6	7	8	1	4	5	3
7	1	4	5	9	3	2	8	6
3	5	8	6	4	2	9	1	7
8	3	5	1	2	4	6	7	9
2	7	1	9	5	6	3	4	8
6	4	9	8	3	7	1	2	5

Solutions

235.

3	1	7	9	4	8	5	2	6
9	5	2	6	1	3	4	7	8
8	4	6	5	7	2	9	1	3
1	8	9	7	5	4	6	3	2
6	7	5	2	3	9	8	4	1
4	2	3	1	8	6	7	9	5
7	9	1	8	2	5	3	6	4
5	6	4	3	9	1	2	8	7
2	3	8	4	6	7	1	5	9

236.

7	1	5	9	8	6	3	4	2
3	9	2	4	5	1	8	6	7
4	6	8	3	2	7	1	9	5
8	5	1	6	4	9	7	2	3
6	3	7	5	1	2	9	8	4
9	2	4	7	3	8	5	1	6
5	7	6	8	9	4	2	3	1
2	8	3	1	6	5	4	7	9
1	4	9	2	7	3	6	5	8

237.

6	8	2	7	9	5	1	4	3
9	3	7	6	1	4	5	8	2
1	5	4	2	8	3	7	6	9
7	6	3	1	5	9	4	2	8
8	1	9	4	3	2	6	5	7
4	2	5	8	6	7	3	9	1
3	4	1	5	2	8	9	7	6
5	9	8	3	7	6	2	1	4
2	7	6	9	4	1	8	3	5

238.

1	6	8	4	9	3	2	5	7
2	9	3	7	5	1	4	8	6
5	7	4	8	6	2	9	1	3
4	5	9	6	3	8	7	2	1
7	3	1	5	2	4	6	9	8
8	2	6	9	1	7	5	3	4
6	8	2	1	7	9	3	4	5
3	4	7	2	8	5	1	6	9
9	1	5	3	4	6	8	7	2

239.

3	7	9	1	6	4	2	8	5
8	4	1	5	2	3	7	6	9
2	5	6	7	8	9	1	3	4
1	3	7	4	5	2	8	9	6
5	9	2	6	7	8	4	1	3
4	6	8	3	9	1	5	7	2
9	8	5	2	3	7	6	4	1
7	2	4	9	1	6	3	5	8
6	1	3	8	4	5	9	2	7

240.

9	2	5	7	1	3	8	4	6
3	7	4	2	6	8	5	9	1
1	6	8	9	5	4	7	3	2
6	8	9	5	4	1	3	2	7
7	1	3	6	9	2	4	5	8
5	4	2	3	8	7	6	1	9
2	9	6	4	7	5	1	8	3
8	5	7	1	3	9	2	6	4
4	3	1	8	2	6	9	7	5

241.

4	3	5	9	6	8	1	7	2
8	9	1	7	3	2	4	5	6
2	6	7	1	4	5	9	3	8
5	7	6	8	2	1	3	9	4
1	8	9	4	5	3	6	2	7
3	2	4	6	9	7	5	8	1
7	5	8	3	1	4	2	6	9
9	1	2	5	8	6	7	4	3
6	4	3	2	7	9	8	1	5

242.

3	7	5	1	4	8	9	2	6
6	2	8	9	5	3	7	4	1
9	4	1	6	2	7	8	5	3
7	1	6	3	9	2	4	8	5
4	8	9	5	7	1	6	3	2
2	5	3	4	8	6	1	7	9
5	3	4	8	6	9	2	1	7
1	9	2	7	3	4	5	6	8
8	6	7	2	1	5	3	9	4

243.

2	5	7	6	9	8	1	3	4
4	3	6	1	5	7	8	2	9
8	1	9	2	3	4	6	7	5
3	4	2	7	1	9	5	8	6
7	8	5	3	4	6	9	1	2
6	9	1	8	2	5	7	4	3
1	6	3	9	7	2	4	5	8
9	2	4	5	8	1	3	6	7
5	7	8	4	6	3	2	9	1

Solutions

244.

8	2	7	3	9	5	4	1	6
1	4	5	6	7	2	9	3	8
3	9	6	8	1	4	5	7	2
2	3	8	9	4	1	7	6	5
4	7	1	5	6	8	3	2	9
6	5	9	7	2	3	1	8	4
9	6	3	4	8	7	2	5	1
5	1	4	2	3	6	8	9	7
7	8	2	1	5	9	6	4	3

245.

7	2	5	4	3	6	9	8	1
4	6	8	9	5	1	3	7	2
9	1	3	2	7	8	4	6	5
3	5	9	1	8	4	6	2	7
2	8	7	3	6	5	1	4	9
1	4	6	7	9	2	5	3	8
5	7	4	6	2	9	8	1	3
8	3	1	5	4	7	2	9	6
6	9	2	8	1	3	7	5	4

246.

6	7	3	5	2	1	9	8	4
5	2	1	8	4	9	7	6	3
4	8	9	7	6	3	5	2	1
2	6	8	9	1	5	3	4	7
9	3	4	2	8	7	1	5	6
1	5	7	4	3	6	2	9	8
3	4	5	1	9	8	6	7	2
7	1	2	6	5	4	8	3	9
8	9	6	3	7	2	4	1	5

247.

8	4	3	1	5	2	9	7	6
5	2	7	6	4	9	1	8	3
6	9	1	8	7	3	4	5	2
4	7	5	9	2	6	3	1	8
2	3	9	5	8	1	7	6	4
1	6	8	7	3	4	5	2	9
9	8	6	3	1	7	2	4	5
7	5	4	2	9	8	6	3	1
3	1	2	4	6	5	8	9	7

248.

1	6	3	4	5	9	8	7	2
4	2	8	6	7	1	3	5	9
5	7	9	2	3	8	6	1	4
9	8	7	1	6	4	5	2	3
2	3	4	7	9	5	1	8	6
6	5	1	8	2	3	4	9	7
8	9	6	5	4	2	7	3	1
3	4	5	9	1	7	2	6	8
7	1	2	3	8	6	9	4	5

249.

1	6	5	7	8	9	2	4	3
3	9	8	5	2	4	1	7	6
7	4	2	1	3	6	8	9	5
8	7	3	6	4	1	9	5	2
9	1	4	2	5	8	3	6	7
5	2	6	9	7	3	4	8	1
6	8	7	4	1	2	5	3	9
2	3	9	8	6	5	7	1	4
4	5	1	3	9	7	6	2	8

250.

8	1	4	6	3	7	9	5	2
7	2	5	1	8	9	6	4	3
9	3	6	4	2	5	7	8	1
4	6	9	8	5	2	1	3	7
1	7	2	9	4	3	5	6	8
3	5	8	7	1	6	4	2	9
2	9	3	5	6	1	8	7	4
5	8	1	2	7	4	3	9	6
6	4	7	3	9	8	2	1	5

251.

4	8	7	3	6	5	9	1	2
3	6	1	9	8	2	4	5	7
9	5	2	4	1	7	6	3	8
5	3	9	2	4	6	8	7	1
7	1	4	5	3	8	2	9	6
6	2	8	1	7	9	3	4	5
8	7	3	6	5	4	1	2	9
1	9	6	7	2	3	5	8	4
2	4	5	8	9	1	7	6	3

252.

4	2	1	3	7	9	5	6	8
7	8	6	4	2	5	9	1	3
9	3	5	8	6	1	7	2	4
6	5	7	2	4	3	1	8	9
3	1	8	7	9	6	4	5	2
2	4	9	1	5	8	6	3	7
8	6	2	9	1	7	3	4	5
5	7	4	6	3	2	8	9	1
1	9	3	5	8	4	2	7	6

Solutions

253.

7	4	2	9	3	5	6	8	1
9	1	5	2	6	8	4	7	3
6	8	3	1	4	7	2	9	5
3	6	1	5	8	2	9	4	7
5	2	8	7	9	4	3	1	6
4	9	7	6	1	3	5	2	8
1	3	4	8	5	9	7	6	2
2	5	6	4	7	1	8	3	9
8	7	9	3	2	6	1	5	4

254.

3	4	2	7	6	1	5	9	8
8	6	9	3	5	2	7	4	1
1	7	5	9	8	4	6	2	3
9	8	7	4	1	5	2	3	6
4	2	1	6	9	3	8	7	5
5	3	6	8	2	7	4	1	9
7	5	3	1	4	6	9	8	2
6	1	8	2	7	9	3	5	4
2	9	4	5	3	8	1	6	7

255.

1	9	8	4	2	5	3	7	6
3	5	6	1	9	7	2	4	8
7	2	4	6	3	8	5	1	9
6	7	5	8	1	9	4	3	2
8	3	2	5	4	6	1	9	7
4	1	9	3	7	2	6	8	5
9	6	1	2	8	4	7	5	3
5	8	3	7	6	1	9	2	4
2	4	7	9	5	3	8	6	1

256.

8	5	9	4	6	2	3	7	1
3	1	2	7	5	8	9	4	6
6	4	7	1	9	3	2	5	8
5	9	8	6	2	7	4	1	3
1	2	3	8	4	5	6	9	7
4	7	6	9	3	1	8	2	5
2	6	1	5	8	4	7	3	9
9	3	5	2	7	6	1	8	4
7	8	4	3	1	9	5	6	2

257.

4	8	9	5	6	7	2	3	1
5	1	6	9	2	3	4	7	8
2	7	3	4	1	8	6	5	9
7	5	4	3	8	9	1	6	2
6	9	2	1	5	4	7	8	3
8	3	1	6	7	2	9	4	5
3	2	7	8	9	6	5	1	4
9	4	5	7	3	1	8	2	6
1	6	8	2	4	5	3	9	7

258.

5	1	4	6	8	7	2	9	3
2	6	9	3	5	1	8	4	7
8	7	3	2	4	9	6	1	5
3	9	6	7	1	8	4	5	2
1	4	5	9	2	6	3	7	8
7	8	2	5	3	4	1	6	9
9	3	1	4	7	2	5	8	6
6	5	8	1	9	3	7	2	4
4	2	7	8	6	5	9	3	1

259.

8	4	1	9	7	2	5	6	3
5	3	7	1	4	6	2	9	8
6	2	9	3	5	8	7	4	1
9	8	3	7	6	1	4	2	5
1	6	2	5	8	4	3	7	9
7	5	4	2	9	3	1	8	6
4	1	6	8	3	7	9	5	2
2	9	8	4	1	5	6	3	7
3	7	5	6	2	9	8	1	4

260.

3	9	8	2	4	7	6	1	5
5	1	7	9	6	3	8	4	2
6	4	2	8	5	1	7	3	9
7	5	4	1	2	9	3	6	8
2	8	6	4	3	5	1	9	7
9	3	1	6	7	8	5	2	4
1	2	5	7	9	6	4	8	3
8	7	9	3	1	4	2	5	6
4	6	3	5	8	2	9	7	1

261.

6	1	4	7	5	8	9	3	2
8	9	7	2	6	3	1	5	4
2	5	3	9	4	1	7	8	6
7	6	9	1	2	5	3	4	8
3	8	5	6	9	4	2	7	1
4	2	1	8	3	7	5	6	9
5	3	8	4	1	2	6	9	7
1	7	6	5	8	9	4	2	3
9	4	2	3	7	6	8	1	5

Solutions

262.

7	5	9	4	8	3	6	1	2
6	8	1	2	9	7	4	5	3
4	2	3	6	5	1	8	9	7
9	3	2	7	1	8	5	4	6
5	6	4	9	3	2	1	7	8
1	7	8	5	4	6	2	3	9
3	1	5	8	2	9	7	6	4
2	9	6	1	7	4	3	8	5
8	4	7	3	6	5	9	2	1

263.

3	4	9	5	8	1	2	6	7
6	1	7	4	9	2	3	8	5
2	5	8	3	6	7	4	1	9
8	2	6	9	1	5	7	4	3
7	9	1	8	3	4	5	2	6
5	3	4	7	2	6	8	9	1
1	8	5	6	4	3	9	7	2
4	7	2	1	5	9	6	3	8
9	6	3	2	7	8	1	5	4

264.

5	7	1	2	9	6	3	8	4
6	8	3	4	1	7	2	9	5
2	9	4	5	8	3	7	1	6
3	4	9	7	5	2	1	6	8
7	1	6	3	4	8	9	5	2
8	2	5	9	6	1	4	3	7
1	3	7	6	2	5	8	4	9
4	5	8	1	7	9	6	2	3
9	6	2	8	3	4	5	7	1

265.

8	3	5	9	4	1	2	6	7
7	2	4	8	5	6	9	1	3
1	9	6	7	2	3	8	4	5
5	7	8	1	6	9	3	2	4
2	6	9	4	3	8	7	5	1
4	1	3	2	7	5	6	9	8
3	5	1	6	9	7	4	8	2
6	8	2	3	1	4	5	7	9
9	4	7	5	8	2	1	3	6

266.

9	7	6	3	4	2	1	5	8
1	2	4	5	6	8	3	7	9
3	8	5	1	7	9	6	2	4
4	9	1	2	8	3	7	6	5
5	6	2	4	1	7	9	8	3
7	3	8	6	9	5	2	4	1
8	1	9	7	2	4	5	3	6
2	4	3	9	5	6	8	1	7
6	5	7	8	3	1	4	9	2

267.

1	4	2	5	7	8	9	6	3
6	7	8	3	4	9	1	5	2
3	5	9	1	6	2	8	4	7
9	2	3	6	5	1	7	8	4
4	1	5	2	8	7	3	9	6
8	6	7	4	9	3	2	1	5
2	3	4	9	1	6	5	7	8
7	9	6	8	3	5	4	2	1
5	8	1	7	2	4	6	3	9

268.

5	1	9	8	3	4	6	2	7
2	8	3	7	1	6	5	9	4
6	7	4	2	5	9	1	8	3
4	5	1	9	8	7	2	3	6
9	2	8	3	6	1	7	4	5
3	6	7	5	4	2	8	1	9
7	3	6	1	9	8	4	5	2
8	9	2	4	7	5	3	6	1
1	4	5	6	2	3	9	7	8

269.

7	9	1	8	2	5	3	4	6
3	2	8	6	7	4	5	9	1
6	4	5	3	9	1	8	7	2
9	1	4	2	8	6	7	3	5
8	6	3	1	5	7	4	2	9
5	7	2	4	3	9	1	6	8
4	5	6	9	1	3	2	8	7
2	3	7	5	6	8	9	1	4
1	8	9	7	4	2	6	5	3

270.

3	1	2	9	5	8	6	7	4
4	5	6	1	7	2	3	9	8
9	8	7	3	6	4	5	2	1
5	2	4	8	3	6	7	1	9
1	7	3	5	2	9	8	4	6
6	9	8	7	4	1	2	5	3
7	6	9	4	8	5	1	3	2
2	4	5	6	1	3	9	8	7
8	3	1	2	9	7	4	6	5

Solutions

271.

2	8	1	7	9	4	5	6	3
7	6	5	3	8	1	9	2	4
3	9	4	6	2	5	7	8	1
5	1	2	9	4	7	6	3	8
4	3	9	5	6	8	1	7	2
8	7	6	2	1	3	4	9	5
6	5	7	4	3	2	8	1	9
1	4	3	8	7	9	2	5	6
9	2	8	1	5	6	3	4	7

272.

1	8	3	2	4	7	9	6	5
2	5	4	6	3	9	8	1	7
7	6	9	8	5	1	2	3	4
8	7	5	9	6	2	3	4	1
6	4	2	7	1	3	5	9	8
9	3	1	4	8	5	6	7	2
3	2	8	1	9	4	7	5	6
5	1	6	3	7	8	4	2	9
4	9	7	5	2	6	1	8	3

273.

4	5	6	9	3	7	2	1	8
3	7	8	5	2	1	6	9	4
1	9	2	4	8	6	3	5	7
6	8	1	3	7	5	4	2	9
5	3	9	1	4	2	7	8	6
7	2	4	6	9	8	5	3	1
2	6	3	8	1	4	9	7	5
9	1	5	7	6	3	8	4	2
8	4	7	2	5	9	1	6	3

274.

4	3	9	2	5	7	6	8	1
6	1	7	4	8	3	2	9	5
8	5	2	1	9	6	7	4	3
2	6	4	8	1	5	9	3	7
5	8	3	9	7	4	1	6	2
7	9	1	3	6	2	8	5	4
1	7	5	6	3	8	4	2	9
9	4	8	5	2	1	3	7	6
3	2	6	7	4	9	5	1	8

275.

4	5	7	8	2	1	3	6	9
9	3	8	4	6	7	2	1	5
2	6	1	3	5	9	7	4	8
7	4	6	1	3	5	9	8	2
1	9	3	7	8	2	4	5	6
5	8	2	6	9	4	1	3	7
6	1	4	2	7	8	5	9	3
8	2	9	5	4	3	6	7	1
3	7	5	9	1	6	8	2	4

276.

3	4	6	9	5	2	1	7	8
2	8	1	7	6	4	3	9	5
5	9	7	1	3	8	4	2	6
1	5	8	6	4	7	9	3	2
6	2	9	5	1	3	7	8	4
4	7	3	8	2	9	5	6	1
7	6	4	2	9	1	8	5	3
9	1	2	3	8	5	6	4	7
8	3	5	4	7	6	2	1	9

277.

7	1	5	3	4	9	8	2	6
2	3	9	6	7	8	4	1	5
8	6	4	5	2	1	7	9	3
6	8	3	9	1	4	2	5	7
5	4	2	8	3	7	9	6	1
9	7	1	2	5	6	3	8	4
1	9	8	4	6	3	5	7	2
3	5	7	1	9	2	6	4	8
4	2	6	7	8	5	1	3	9

278.

1	2	4	5	8	7	3	9	6
5	6	3	9	1	2	8	7	4
7	8	9	3	6	4	5	2	1
8	3	7	4	9	5	1	6	2
6	9	5	1	2	8	4	3	7
2	4	1	7	3	6	9	8	5
4	5	8	6	7	3	2	1	9
9	7	2	8	4	1	6	5	3
3	1	6	2	5	9	7	4	8

279.

8	9	7	2	6	3	4	1	5
4	1	2	9	5	7	6	8	3
3	6	5	8	1	4	7	9	2
9	8	3	4	2	1	5	6	7
2	7	6	3	9	5	8	4	1
1	5	4	7	8	6	2	3	9
6	3	1	5	4	2	9	7	8
5	4	9	1	7	8	3	2	6
7	2	8	6	3	9	1	5	4

Solutions

280.

4	1	9	8	3	7	6	5	2
3	5	2	6	4	1	8	7	9
6	8	7	9	5	2	1	3	4
1	3	6	4	2	8	5	9	7
5	7	4	1	6	9	3	2	8
2	9	8	5	7	3	4	1	6
9	6	3	2	8	5	7	4	1
8	2	5	7	1	4	9	6	3
7	4	1	3	9	6	2	8	5

281.

8	2	6	3	4	7	5	1	9
3	1	5	8	2	9	4	7	6
4	7	9	1	5	6	2	8	3
7	6	8	5	9	4	3	2	1
9	5	2	7	3	1	8	6	4
1	4	3	6	8	2	7	9	5
2	8	4	9	6	5	1	3	7
5	9	1	2	7	3	6	4	8
6	3	7	4	1	8	9	5	2

282.

5	3	4	7	2	1	6	9	8
1	7	8	9	6	5	4	3	2
9	2	6	8	3	4	5	1	7
8	6	7	5	1	2	9	4	3
3	9	1	6	4	8	7	2	5
4	5	2	3	7	9	8	6	1
2	8	5	4	9	3	1	7	6
6	4	3	1	5	7	2	8	9
7	1	9	2	8	6	3	5	4

283.

7	3	1	2	9	6	4	8	5
8	9	2	3	5	4	1	6	7
5	4	6	7	1	8	9	2	3
1	7	4	5	8	2	3	9	6
6	2	5	1	3	9	7	4	8
3	8	9	6	4	7	5	1	2
2	1	7	4	6	3	8	5	9
9	5	3	8	2	1	6	7	4
4	6	8	9	7	5	2	3	1

284.

8	1	7	9	4	2	3	5	6
4	5	2	6	8	3	9	7	1
9	3	6	1	7	5	2	4	8
7	2	9	5	1	6	4	8	3
1	8	5	4	3	9	7	6	2
6	4	3	8	2	7	5	1	9
3	7	4	2	6	8	1	9	5
5	6	1	3	9	4	8	2	7
2	9	8	7	5	1	6	3	4

285.

3	4	6	9	2	7	8	5	1
2	5	7	8	1	4	6	9	3
1	8	9	3	6	5	2	4	7
6	1	3	2	4	9	7	8	5
7	2	4	5	3	8	1	6	9
8	9	5	1	7	6	3	2	4
4	3	8	7	9	2	5	1	6
5	6	1	4	8	3	9	7	2
9	7	2	6	5	1	4	3	8

286.

7	2	4	5	1	3	8	6	9
3	6	9	4	2	8	1	7	5
8	1	5	7	9	6	2	4	3
4	3	6	9	7	1	5	2	8
1	7	8	2	3	5	6	9	4
5	9	2	8	6	4	3	1	7
9	5	7	6	8	2	4	3	1
2	8	1	3	4	7	9	5	6
6	4	3	1	5	9	7	8	2

287.

3	5	4	6	1	9	8	7	2
6	1	8	3	7	2	9	5	4
7	9	2	8	5	4	3	1	6
9	6	7	5	3	1	2	4	8
2	8	3	9	4	7	1	6	5
5	4	1	2	8	6	7	9	3
8	7	9	4	2	5	6	3	1
1	3	5	7	6	8	4	2	9
4	2	6	1	9	3	5	8	7

288.

8	7	6	1	5	9	4	2	3
1	5	3	8	2	4	9	6	7
4	9	2	6	7	3	8	1	5
9	8	5	2	3	6	7	4	1
2	3	4	7	1	5	6	8	9
6	1	7	9	4	8	3	5	2
7	2	9	4	8	1	5	3	6
5	4	1	3	6	7	2	9	8
3	6	8	5	9	2	1	7	4

289.

3	8	1	4	6	9	7	2	5
7	4	2	3	5	1	6	9	8
6	5	9	2	8	7	3	4	1
2	7	4	8	3	5	1	6	9
1	6	8	9	7	4	5	3	2
9	3	5	6	1	2	8	7	4
5	9	7	1	2	6	4	8	3
4	1	3	7	9	8	2	5	6
8	2	6	5	4	3	9	1	7

290.

9	2	6	3	8	4	5	1	7
8	3	4	5	1	7	6	9	2
7	1	5	2	9	6	3	8	4
4	6	1	9	3	2	8	7	5
2	7	9	4	5	8	1	6	3
5	8	3	7	6	1	2	4	9
6	5	7	8	4	3	9	2	1
3	4	8	1	2	9	7	5	6
1	9	2	6	7	5	4	3	8

291.

1	4	2	6	9	8	7	5	3
6	8	5	4	7	3	2	9	1
9	7	3	2	1	5	8	6	4
8	6	7	9	2	1	3	4	5
4	3	1	7	5	6	9	2	8
2	5	9	8	3	4	1	7	6
5	9	8	3	4	2	6	1	7
3	2	4	1	6	7	5	8	9
7	1	6	5	8	9	4	3	2

292.

6	8	4	1	5	3	9	7	2
7	2	5	6	9	8	1	4	3
1	9	3	7	2	4	5	6	8
3	1	8	5	6	9	4	2	7
2	5	6	4	3	7	8	1	9
4	7	9	8	1	2	6	3	5
9	4	1	2	7	5	3	8	6
5	6	7	3	8	1	2	9	4
8	3	2	9	4	6	7	5	1

293.

3	6	8	9	5	1	7	2	4
1	7	5	3	2	4	8	6	9
4	2	9	6	7	8	3	5	1
5	4	3	7	8	6	9	1	2
7	8	6	2	1	9	5	4	3
9	1	2	5	4	3	6	8	7
8	9	4	1	6	7	2	3	5
2	3	1	8	9	5	4	7	6
6	5	7	4	3	2	1	9	8

294.

5	6	3	7	8	9	2	1	4
1	8	2	4	5	6	7	9	3
7	9	4	3	2	1	5	6	8
3	5	9	8	1	2	4	7	6
4	1	8	6	3	7	9	5	2
6	2	7	9	4	5	3	8	1
2	4	6	5	9	8	1	3	7
8	3	5	1	7	4	6	2	9
9	7	1	2	6	3	8	4	5

295.

8	1	7	2	4	6	9	5	3
9	2	3	5	1	7	4	6	8
4	6	5	8	3	9	1	2	7
1	3	8	7	6	2	5	4	9
6	5	4	1	9	3	7	8	2
7	9	2	4	8	5	6	3	1
3	4	9	6	7	8	2	1	5
5	7	1	3	2	4	8	9	6
2	8	6	9	5	1	3	7	4

296.

1	7	2	4	9	5	8	6	3
4	3	5	2	6	8	1	9	7
6	8	9	3	7	1	5	2	4
5	1	3	8	2	6	4	7	9
2	6	7	1	4	9	3	8	5
9	4	8	5	3	7	6	1	2
3	9	4	6	1	2	7	5	8
8	2	6	7	5	3	9	4	1
7	5	1	9	8	4	2	3	6

297.

1	8	9	6	5	3	4	2	7
3	7	4	1	8	2	9	6	5
5	6	2	4	9	7	8	1	3
9	1	6	2	3	4	7	5	8
2	4	3	5	7	8	6	9	1
8	5	7	9	6	1	3	4	2
7	9	1	8	4	5	2	3	6
4	3	5	7	2	6	1	8	9
6	2	8	3	1	9	5	7	4

Solutions

298.

4	2	7	1	6	5	8	3	9
1	6	9	3	8	2	4	7	5
3	5	8	7	9	4	1	6	2
2	9	4	8	1	7	3	5	6
7	8	1	5	3	6	2	9	4
6	3	5	2	4	9	7	1	8
5	1	2	9	7	8	6	4	3
9	7	6	4	2	3	5	8	1
8	4	3	6	5	1	9	2	7

299.

1	9	3	2	6	7	4	5	8
4	5	6	9	1	8	2	7	3
7	8	2	5	3	4	9	6	1
5	3	1	8	9	2	6	4	7
8	2	9	4	7	6	3	1	5
6	7	4	1	5	3	8	2	9
2	6	5	3	8	1	7	9	4
3	1	7	6	4	9	5	8	2
9	4	8	7	2	5	1	3	6

300.

1	5	7	6	9	8	2	4	3
4	8	9	1	3	2	7	6	5
3	6	2	4	5	7	9	8	1
7	3	5	8	1	9	4	2	6
2	9	4	3	6	5	1	7	8
6	1	8	2	7	4	3	5	9
5	2	6	9	4	1	8	3	7
8	7	1	5	2	3	6	9	4
9	4	3	7	8	6	5	1	2

301.

3	5	1	9	6	8	7	4	2
7	8	6	1	2	4	5	9	3
9	2	4	7	5	3	8	6	1
2	9	8	5	4	1	6	3	7
5	1	3	6	7	2	9	8	4
6	4	7	8	3	9	1	2	5
4	6	5	2	8	7	3	1	9
1	7	2	3	9	6	4	5	8
8	3	9	4	1	5	2	7	6

302.

9	7	3	5	1	2	4	6	8
1	4	8	6	9	7	3	5	2
6	2	5	3	4	8	7	1	9
2	9	7	1	3	4	6	8	5
5	8	6	7	2	9	1	3	4
3	1	4	8	5	6	9	2	7
7	3	1	4	8	5	2	9	6
4	5	9	2	6	3	8	7	1
8	6	2	9	7	1	5	4	3

303.

2	4	6	1	3	8	5	7	9
1	3	7	9	4	5	8	6	2
8	9	5	7	6	2	3	4	1
9	6	2	8	7	3	4	1	5
7	8	3	5	1	4	2	9	6
4	5	1	2	9	6	7	3	8
5	7	9	4	8	1	6	2	3
3	2	4	6	5	9	1	8	7
6	1	8	3	2	7	9	5	4

304.

8	5	1	4	2	6	7	9	3
2	4	7	5	9	3	8	1	6
3	6	9	1	7	8	5	2	4
9	7	8	3	1	5	6	4	2
4	1	6	7	8	2	9	3	5
5	2	3	9	6	4	1	7	8
6	9	2	8	4	1	3	5	7
7	8	5	2	3	9	4	6	1
1	3	4	6	5	7	2	8	9

305.

2	4	1	5	7	9	6	3	8
6	3	8	1	4	2	9	5	7
5	7	9	3	6	8	2	1	4
4	9	7	2	5	6	3	8	1
1	6	5	9	8	3	7	4	2
3	8	2	4	1	7	5	6	9
9	5	6	8	2	4	1	7	3
7	2	4	6	3	1	8	9	5
8	1	3	7	9	5	4	2	6

306.

5	9	2	7	1	4	8	6	3
7	6	1	3	9	8	2	5	4
4	3	8	2	6	5	1	7	9
9	2	4	5	3	6	7	1	8
8	7	3	9	2	1	6	4	5
6	1	5	8	4	7	9	3	2
3	5	7	1	8	9	4	2	6
1	4	9	6	5	2	3	8	7
2	8	6	4	7	3	5	9	1

Solutions

307.

3	9	5	7	6	4	2	8	1
1	7	4	8	3	2	6	9	5
2	8	6	5	1	9	4	3	7
7	6	1	9	8	3	5	4	2
8	2	9	4	5	6	1	7	3
4	5	3	1	2	7	9	6	8
5	4	2	6	7	8	3	1	9
9	1	7	3	4	5	8	2	6
6	3	8	2	9	1	7	5	4

308.

2	8	7	1	5	4	9	6	3
9	6	1	8	3	2	7	5	4
4	5	3	7	9	6	2	1	8
5	4	2	3	6	1	8	9	7
6	3	9	5	7	8	4	2	1
1	7	8	4	2	9	6	3	5
7	1	6	9	8	5	3	4	2
8	9	5	2	4	3	1	7	6
3	2	4	6	1	7	5	8	9

309.

6	2	7	3	9	8	4	5	1
8	3	9	5	1	4	6	7	2
5	4	1	7	6	2	8	9	3
7	9	5	6	8	3	2	1	4
2	1	6	4	7	9	3	8	5
3	8	4	1	2	5	9	6	7
4	7	2	9	5	6	1	3	8
9	5	8	2	3	1	7	4	6
1	6	3	8	4	7	5	2	9

310.

6	1	3	5	8	9	2	7	4
9	4	8	1	7	2	3	6	5
5	7	2	4	6	3	9	1	8
8	5	4	6	9	7	1	2	3
3	6	9	2	5	1	8	4	7
7	2	1	3	4	8	5	9	6
4	9	7	8	1	5	6	3	2
1	3	5	7	2	6	4	8	9
2	8	6	9	3	4	7	5	1

311.

6	8	3	4	1	7	2	5	9
1	5	9	8	3	2	4	7	6
2	4	7	6	5	9	1	3	8
5	7	1	9	6	4	8	2	3
8	3	4	2	7	1	9	6	5
9	6	2	3	8	5	7	4	1
4	2	8	5	9	6	3	1	7
3	1	5	7	2	8	6	9	4
7	9	6	1	4	3	5	8	2

312.

1	6	7	4	8	2	9	5	3
9	8	4	5	7	3	1	2	6
2	5	3	6	9	1	4	7	8
4	7	5	2	1	6	8	3	9
6	1	8	9	3	5	7	4	2
3	9	2	8	4	7	6	1	5
7	3	6	1	2	8	5	9	4
5	4	1	3	6	9	2	8	7
8	2	9	7	5	4	3	6	1

313.

7	1	8	9	3	6	4	5	2
9	5	3	2	4	8	6	7	1
4	6	2	7	5	1	8	9	3
1	2	6	5	9	7	3	4	8
5	8	9	4	6	3	2	1	7
3	4	7	8	1	2	9	6	5
2	9	4	3	7	5	1	8	6
8	7	1	6	2	9	5	3	4
6	3	5	1	8	4	7	2	9

314.

2	3	7	4	8	6	1	5	9
8	9	1	3	5	7	4	6	2
6	5	4	9	2	1	8	7	3
3	7	9	1	4	2	6	8	5
4	1	8	6	9	5	3	2	7
5	6	2	8	7	3	9	4	1
9	4	5	7	1	8	2	3	6
7	8	3	2	6	9	5	1	4
1	2	6	5	3	4	7	9	8

315.

9	1	6	5	8	7	2	3	4
2	8	5	4	1	3	9	6	7
4	7	3	9	2	6	8	5	1
1	3	9	2	6	8	4	7	5
5	2	4	1	7	9	6	8	3
8	6	7	3	4	5	1	9	2
6	9	1	7	3	2	5	4	8
7	5	2	8	9	4	3	1	6
3	4	8	6	5	1	7	2	9

Solutions

316.

2	5	9	3	6	8	1	4	7
8	1	4	9	7	5	2	3	6
6	7	3	2	1	4	5	8	9
5	2	6	7	8	9	4	1	3
9	3	8	1	4	6	7	2	5
7	4	1	5	2	3	9	6	8
4	6	7	8	5	1	3	9	2
1	9	5	6	3	2	8	7	4
3	8	2	4	9	7	6	5	1

317.

4	2	8	6	1	3	7	5	9
1	7	9	5	8	4	6	3	2
6	3	5	2	9	7	4	8	1
7	5	2	9	4	8	1	6	3
3	6	4	1	5	2	9	7	8
9	8	1	7	3	6	5	2	4
5	4	6	8	2	1	3	9	7
2	9	3	4	7	5	8	1	6
8	1	7	3	6	9	2	4	5

318.

4	5	9	6	1	8	2	7	3
1	6	3	2	7	9	8	4	5
8	7	2	3	5	4	9	6	1
7	3	1	8	9	5	6	2	4
6	9	5	7	4	2	3	1	8
2	4	8	1	6	3	7	5	9
5	1	7	9	3	6	4	8	2
3	8	6	4	2	1	5	9	7
9	2	4	5	8	7	1	3	6

319.

9	6	5	3	8	1	7	4	2
3	2	1	9	4	7	6	5	8
4	8	7	5	2	6	3	1	9
2	5	8	4	9	3	1	7	6
6	1	9	7	5	8	2	3	4
7	3	4	6	1	2	8	9	5
5	7	3	8	6	4	9	2	1
1	9	6	2	3	5	4	8	7
8	4	2	1	7	9	5	6	3

320.

6	2	7	8	9	1	3	5	4
8	9	1	5	3	4	2	7	6
4	5	3	7	2	6	1	8	9
7	4	8	2	1	5	9	6	3
5	6	2	3	4	9	8	1	7
3	1	9	6	7	8	4	2	5
1	7	4	9	6	2	5	3	8
2	8	6	4	5	3	7	9	1
9	3	5	1	8	7	6	4	2

321.

3	1	8	5	9	6	4	2	7
6	7	2	4	8	1	9	3	5
5	4	9	2	3	7	1	8	6
7	6	3	1	2	5	8	4	9
8	2	4	3	6	9	5	7	1
1	9	5	7	4	8	2	6	3
2	5	1	8	7	3	6	9	4
9	8	7	6	5	4	3	1	2
4	3	6	9	1	2	7	5	8

322.

6	1	9	2	3	4	7	5	8
2	4	8	5	7	1	6	9	3
5	3	7	6	8	9	4	2	1
8	2	3	7	5	6	1	4	9
1	9	5	3	4	2	8	7	6
7	6	4	9	1	8	5	3	2
9	5	2	1	6	7	3	8	4
3	8	6	4	2	5	9	1	7
4	7	1	8	9	3	2	6	5

323.

7	8	2	5	1	9	6	3	4
1	9	6	4	8	3	5	7	2
3	5	4	6	7	2	8	9	1
2	1	8	9	6	4	3	5	7
4	7	9	8	3	5	2	1	6
6	3	5	7	2	1	9	4	8
9	4	1	2	5	8	7	6	3
5	2	7	3	4	6	1	8	9
8	6	3	1	9	7	4	2	5

324.

3	7	5	9	2	4	6	8	1
8	1	4	6	3	5	7	2	9
9	2	6	1	8	7	5	4	3
6	4	2	3	7	1	8	9	5
5	3	1	2	9	8	4	6	7
7	9	8	4	5	6	1	3	2
1	5	9	8	6	3	2	7	4
2	8	7	5	4	9	3	1	6
4	6	3	7	1	2	9	5	8

Solutions

325.

2	6	8	3	4	9	1	7	5
9	5	1	8	2	7	3	4	6
7	4	3	6	5	1	8	9	2
8	1	7	9	6	4	2	5	3
3	2	5	7	1	8	9	6	4
4	9	6	5	3	2	7	8	1
5	8	4	2	9	3	6	1	7
1	3	9	4	7	6	5	2	8
6	7	2	1	8	5	4	3	9

326.

5	7	3	9	2	6	8	4	1
2	4	1	7	8	5	9	3	6
8	6	9	3	4	1	2	5	7
3	1	2	8	6	4	7	9	5
4	5	7	2	1	9	6	8	3
6	9	8	5	3	7	1	2	4
9	3	4	1	7	2	5	6	8
1	8	5	6	9	3	4	7	2
7	2	6	4	5	8	3	1	9

327.

3	8	5	4	1	9	6	7	2
7	2	4	3	5	6	1	9	8
9	1	6	2	8	7	3	4	5
4	3	8	5	9	1	7	2	6
6	9	2	7	3	4	5	8	1
1	5	7	6	2	8	9	3	4
5	7	3	1	4	2	8	6	9
2	6	9	8	7	5	4	1	3
8	4	1	9	6	3	2	5	7

328.

8	4	2	7	5	6	9	3	1
1	6	3	4	9	8	2	7	5
9	5	7	1	2	3	4	8	6
4	3	6	2	7	5	8	1	9
7	1	5	3	8	9	6	4	2
2	8	9	6	1	4	7	5	3
3	9	8	5	4	2	1	6	7
6	2	1	8	3	7	5	9	4
5	7	4	9	6	1	3	2	8

329.

9	2	6	3	8	4	1	5	7
4	1	7	6	5	2	3	9	8
8	3	5	7	9	1	4	2	6
6	9	8	1	2	3	7	4	5
7	5	2	4	6	8	9	1	3
1	4	3	9	7	5	8	6	2
3	6	1	2	4	7	5	8	9
5	7	9	8	1	6	2	3	4
2	8	4	5	3	9	6	7	1

330.

9	8	5	6	4	1	2	7	3
3	7	4	9	2	5	6	8	1
6	2	1	8	7	3	4	9	5
1	3	8	2	5	7	9	4	6
4	5	2	1	6	9	7	3	8
7	6	9	4	3	8	5	1	2
2	1	3	5	9	4	8	6	7
5	9	7	3	8	6	1	2	4
8	4	6	7	1	2	3	5	9

331.

7	5	3	4	9	1	8	6	2
9	2	8	7	6	5	4	3	1
6	1	4	3	2	8	7	9	5
5	9	6	8	4	3	1	2	7
4	8	2	1	7	9	6	5	3
1	3	7	6	5	2	9	8	4
3	7	5	9	8	4	2	1	6
2	4	9	5	1	6	3	7	8
8	6	1	2	3	7	5	4	9

332.

4	6	2	9	5	7	3	1	8
9	3	8	1	6	4	7	5	2
1	5	7	2	8	3	6	9	4
5	2	3	6	4	9	8	7	1
7	9	4	8	3	1	2	6	5
6	8	1	5	7	2	9	4	3
2	7	9	4	1	8	5	3	6
8	4	6	3	9	5	1	2	7
3	1	5	7	2	6	4	8	9

333.

7	1	8	5	9	6	2	4	3
5	6	4	2	3	7	9	8	1
3	2	9	4	8	1	6	7	5
8	4	3	7	1	2	5	6	9
2	9	7	8	6	5	3	1	4
1	5	6	3	4	9	7	2	8
6	7	1	9	5	4	8	3	2
9	3	2	1	7	8	4	5	6
4	8	5	6	2	3	1	9	7

Solutions

334.

3	1	6	5	2	9	7	4	8
2	5	8	3	4	7	1	6	9
7	9	4	8	1	6	5	2	3
1	7	9	2	5	4	3	8	6
5	4	2	6	8	3	9	1	7
8	6	3	7	9	1	4	5	2
6	2	7	4	3	5	8	9	1
4	3	1	9	6	8	2	7	5
9	8	5	1	7	2	6	3	4

335.

7	8	6	4	9	3	5	2	1
3	1	4	5	2	6	7	8	9
9	5	2	8	1	7	6	4	3
5	2	1	7	6	8	3	9	4
8	9	7	3	4	1	2	6	5
4	6	3	2	5	9	8	1	7
1	4	5	6	3	2	9	7	8
6	3	8	9	7	4	1	5	2
2	7	9	1	8	5	4	3	6

336.

8	9	7	2	5	4	3	1	6
5	2	4	6	1	3	8	9	7
1	6	3	7	9	8	2	5	4
7	8	2	5	4	6	9	3	1
9	1	6	3	2	7	5	4	8
4	3	5	1	8	9	6	7	2
2	5	9	4	6	1	7	8	3
6	7	1	8	3	5	4	2	9
3	4	8	9	7	2	1	6	5

337.

2	8	5	9	3	7	4	6	1
6	1	9	8	2	4	7	3	5
4	3	7	6	5	1	8	2	9
5	2	8	7	9	6	1	4	3
1	9	3	2	4	8	5	7	6
7	4	6	3	1	5	2	9	8
3	7	4	1	8	9	6	5	2
8	5	2	4	6	3	9	1	7
9	6	1	5	7	2	3	8	4

338.

1	2	3	7	8	6	4	9	5
9	4	7	1	2	5	8	3	6
6	8	5	3	9	4	7	2	1
7	3	8	2	5	1	6	4	9
2	6	1	8	4	9	3	5	7
4	5	9	6	3	7	1	8	2
8	7	4	9	6	2	5	1	3
5	9	6	4	1	3	2	7	8
3	1	2	5	7	8	9	6	4

339.

6	4	8	2	9	5	3	1	7
7	9	3	8	4	1	2	6	5
2	1	5	7	6	3	9	8	4
8	2	6	4	3	7	5	9	1
9	3	4	1	5	8	6	7	2
5	7	1	6	2	9	8	4	3
4	5	2	9	1	6	7	3	8
1	8	9	3	7	2	4	5	6
3	6	7	5	8	4	1	2	9

340.

4	6	7	5	3	8	2	9	1
8	9	5	4	1	2	3	7	6
3	2	1	7	9	6	8	5	4
1	7	9	2	4	3	5	6	8
5	8	6	1	7	9	4	2	3
2	3	4	6	8	5	7	1	9
9	4	2	3	5	1	6	8	7
7	5	8	9	6	4	1	3	2
6	1	3	8	2	7	9	4	5

341.

2	3	8	6	7	1	9	4	5
6	9	1	4	2	5	3	7	8
5	7	4	9	8	3	6	2	1
1	5	3	2	9	4	8	6	7
7	4	6	5	1	8	2	3	9
9	8	2	7	3	6	5	1	4
3	6	7	1	5	9	4	8	2
4	2	9	8	6	7	1	5	3
8	1	5	3	4	2	7	9	6

342.

9	5	4	1	8	6	7	2	3
7	1	2	5	3	9	8	6	4
8	3	6	7	2	4	1	5	9
3	4	9	2	6	8	5	1	7
1	7	8	9	5	3	6	4	2
6	2	5	4	7	1	3	9	8
2	6	7	8	9	5	4	3	1
5	8	1	3	4	2	9	7	6
4	9	3	6	1	7	2	8	5

Solutions

343.

3	7	4	8	6	2	1	5	9
8	2	9	1	7	5	3	6	4
1	5	6	9	4	3	7	8	2
6	8	1	3	5	4	2	9	7
5	9	2	7	1	8	6	4	3
4	3	7	2	9	6	5	1	8
9	6	5	4	3	7	8	2	1
7	1	8	6	2	9	4	3	5
2	4	3	5	8	1	9	7	6

344.

6	5	3	4	9	8	7	1	2
4	9	1	7	3	2	6	8	5
7	8	2	6	1	5	9	3	4
3	2	4	5	7	9	8	6	1
9	1	6	2	8	4	5	7	3
5	7	8	3	6	1	4	2	9
2	4	7	8	5	3	1	9	6
1	6	5	9	2	7	3	4	8
8	3	9	1	4	6	2	5	7

345.

2	9	4	8	5	1	7	6	3
7	8	6	2	3	4	9	5	1
5	1	3	9	7	6	2	8	4
4	6	7	1	2	8	3	9	5
1	2	9	5	4	3	6	7	8
8	3	5	6	9	7	4	1	2
3	4	1	7	8	9	5	2	6
6	7	2	4	1	5	8	3	9
9	5	8	3	6	2	1	4	7

346.

7	5	3	8	4	6	1	9	2
9	2	4	1	7	5	6	8	3
6	8	1	9	2	3	4	5	7
5	3	8	6	1	2	9	7	4
1	7	2	4	9	8	3	6	5
4	6	9	3	5	7	8	2	1
2	9	6	7	3	4	5	1	8
3	1	7	5	8	9	2	4	6
8	4	5	2	6	1	7	3	9

347.

5	6	8	2	3	1	4	7	9
1	4	3	5	9	7	2	8	6
9	2	7	8	4	6	5	3	1
2	7	1	4	6	9	8	5	3
3	5	9	7	1	8	6	2	4
4	8	6	3	2	5	1	9	7
6	3	2	9	5	4	7	1	8
8	1	5	6	7	3	9	4	2
7	9	4	1	8	2	3	6	5

348.

1	4	8	9	2	3	5	6	7
7	2	3	5	6	8	1	4	9
9	5	6	4	1	7	3	2	8
5	7	9	2	3	6	8	1	4
3	1	2	8	9	4	6	7	5
8	6	4	1	7	5	9	3	2
2	3	1	7	8	9	4	5	6
6	9	5	3	4	2	7	8	1
4	8	7	6	5	1	2	9	3

349.

9	4	7	1	5	2	8	6	3
1	8	5	7	3	6	4	9	2
3	2	6	9	8	4	5	7	1
7	1	9	4	6	3	2	5	8
4	6	2	8	7	5	3	1	9
5	3	8	2	1	9	7	4	6
2	9	1	3	4	7	6	8	5
6	7	3	5	9	8	1	2	4
8	5	4	6	2	1	9	3	7

350.

3	4	6	5	9	7	8	2	1
9	1	7	2	8	6	3	5	4
5	8	2	4	3	1	6	9	7
2	5	8	9	4	3	7	1	6
4	6	9	7	1	5	2	3	8
7	3	1	6	2	8	9	4	5
6	2	3	8	5	4	1	7	9
1	7	4	3	6	9	5	8	2
8	9	5	1	7	2	4	6	3

351.

3	2	6	8	9	5	4	1	7
5	4	9	6	1	7	2	8	3
1	8	7	2	4	3	9	6	5
9	3	2	4	7	8	1	5	6
6	5	8	1	3	2	7	9	4
4	7	1	9	5	6	8	3	2
7	9	5	3	2	1	6	4	8
2	6	4	5	8	9	3	7	1
8	1	3	7	6	4	5	2	9

Solutions

352.

6	1	8	7	2	3	4	5	9
2	7	4	8	9	5	3	1	6
5	3	9	4	1	6	2	7	8
4	8	1	2	7	9	5	6	3
3	6	2	5	4	1	9	8	7
7	9	5	6	3	8	1	2	4
9	4	7	1	6	2	8	3	5
1	5	6	3	8	4	7	9	2
8	2	3	9	5	7	6	4	1

353.

1	4	3	5	8	2	9	7	6
2	6	7	4	1	9	3	5	8
5	9	8	3	6	7	1	2	4
3	8	6	7	4	1	2	9	5
7	2	5	8	9	6	4	3	1
9	1	4	2	5	3	6	8	7
4	3	2	1	7	5	8	6	9
8	5	9	6	2	4	7	1	3
6	7	1	9	3	8	5	4	2

354.

9	5	6	3	2	8	1	4	7
4	1	8	9	7	5	3	2	6
2	3	7	4	6	1	8	5	9
8	9	2	1	4	6	7	3	5
1	6	4	5	3	7	2	9	8
3	7	5	8	9	2	4	6	1
5	8	3	2	1	9	6	7	4
7	2	9	6	8	4	5	1	3
6	4	1	7	5	3	9	8	2

355.

6	7	3	2	9	8	1	4	5
1	8	5	4	7	3	9	6	2
2	4	9	6	1	5	8	3	7
8	5	2	7	6	1	4	9	3
4	3	7	5	8	9	2	1	6
9	6	1	3	4	2	7	5	8
7	2	4	1	3	6	5	8	9
3	1	8	9	5	7	6	2	4
5	9	6	8	2	4	3	7	1

356.

2	9	8	6	4	5	1	7	3
3	1	4	8	9	7	5	6	2
6	5	7	1	2	3	4	9	8
7	4	2	9	3	1	6	8	5
1	6	5	4	7	8	3	2	9
9	8	3	2	5	6	7	1	4
5	3	6	7	8	9	2	4	1
8	2	1	5	6	4	9	3	7
4	7	9	3	1	2	8	5	6

357.

5	3	6	9	4	7	1	8	2
2	1	7	6	8	3	4	5	9
8	9	4	5	2	1	7	6	3
3	6	5	1	7	2	8	9	4
7	8	9	3	6	4	2	1	5
1	4	2	8	9	5	6	3	7
6	2	3	4	1	9	5	7	8
9	7	8	2	5	6	3	4	1
4	5	1	7	3	8	9	2	6

358.

2	9	8	1	5	3	4	7	6
7	1	5	4	8	6	2	9	3
4	3	6	7	9	2	5	8	1
3	8	9	2	1	5	7	6	4
6	5	2	3	4	7	8	1	9
1	7	4	8	6	9	3	5	2
9	2	1	5	3	8	6	4	7
5	4	3	6	7	1	9	2	8
8	6	7	9	2	4	1	3	5

359.

4	2	3	8	7	6	1	9	5
5	1	6	9	4	3	2	7	8
9	8	7	2	1	5	3	4	6
7	5	8	6	3	4	9	2	1
1	3	4	5	2	9	8	6	7
6	9	2	1	8	7	4	5	3
2	4	1	7	5	8	6	3	9
3	6	5	4	9	1	7	8	2
8	7	9	3	6	2	5	1	4

360.

8	2	9	5	7	3	1	4	6
7	6	4	1	8	2	3	9	5
5	1	3	9	6	4	8	2	7
3	9	7	6	4	5	2	8	1
6	4	5	8	2	1	9	7	3
1	8	2	3	9	7	6	5	4
2	3	1	7	5	8	4	6	9
4	5	6	2	3	9	7	1	8
9	7	8	4	1	6	5	3	2

Solutions

361.

8	1	9	4	7	2	6	5	3
3	7	2	1	6	5	4	8	9
6	4	5	3	9	8	1	7	2
1	3	8	5	4	9	7	2	6
5	6	4	2	3	7	8	9	1
2	9	7	6	8	1	5	3	4
7	2	3	8	1	6	9	4	5
9	5	6	7	2	4	3	1	8
4	8	1	9	5	3	2	6	7

362.

6	7	1	3	9	2	5	4	8
8	5	4	1	7	6	9	3	2
3	9	2	8	5	4	6	1	7
7	1	8	4	6	9	2	5	3
9	3	6	2	8	5	4	7	1
2	4	5	7	1	3	8	9	6
1	8	9	6	4	7	3	2	5
4	2	7	5	3	8	1	6	9
5	6	3	9	2	1	7	8	4

363.

3	1	7	6	2	8	4	9	5
5	8	4	1	3	9	6	2	7
2	6	9	4	5	7	8	1	3
4	3	1	9	8	5	7	6	2
7	5	2	3	1	6	9	8	4
6	9	8	2	7	4	5	3	1
9	7	3	8	4	1	2	5	6
8	2	5	7	6	3	1	4	9
1	4	6	5	9	2	3	7	8

364.

5	3	8	1	9	7	4	6	2
4	9	6	3	2	5	1	7	8
2	7	1	4	8	6	9	3	5
1	5	9	8	6	3	7	2	4
3	4	2	9	7	1	5	8	6
6	8	7	2	5	4	3	1	9
8	1	3	5	4	2	6	9	7
7	2	5	6	3	9	8	4	1
9	6	4	7	1	8	2	5	3

365.

8	1	3	2	6	5	9	4	7
2	9	5	3	7	4	1	8	6
4	6	7	8	1	9	3	5	2
3	4	6	9	2	7	8	1	5
9	5	1	6	8	3	2	7	4
7	8	2	5	4	1	6	3	9
6	7	8	4	3	2	5	9	1
5	3	4	1	9	6	7	2	8
1	2	9	7	5	8	4	6	3

366.

4	2	6	7	8	9	3	1	5
3	9	5	1	6	4	8	7	2
7	1	8	2	5	3	9	4	6
6	3	9	8	2	7	1	5	4
5	4	7	9	1	6	2	8	3
1	8	2	4	3	5	7	6	9
9	6	1	5	7	2	4	3	8
2	7	3	6	4	8	5	9	1
8	5	4	3	9	1	6	2	7

367.

4	3	8	2	1	5	6	7	9
5	7	9	3	4	6	1	8	2
6	1	2	7	9	8	4	3	5
1	6	7	9	5	3	2	4	8
8	4	3	1	7	2	9	5	6
9	2	5	8	6	4	7	1	3
2	8	4	6	3	1	5	9	7
3	9	1	5	2	7	8	6	4
7	5	6	4	8	9	3	2	1

368.

5	4	6	1	9	8	7	2	3
7	9	2	6	3	5	1	4	8
3	8	1	7	2	4	6	5	9
9	1	4	3	8	7	2	6	5
8	2	7	5	6	9	3	1	4
6	5	3	2	4	1	8	9	7
2	6	5	4	7	3	9	8	1
4	3	8	9	1	6	5	7	2
1	7	9	8	5	2	4	3	6

369.

6	7	1	8	5	9	4	2	3
5	4	8	3	7	2	9	1	6
9	2	3	4	1	6	8	7	5
2	1	5	6	4	7	3	8	9
4	8	9	2	3	1	5	6	7
7	3	6	9	8	5	2	4	1
1	9	4	5	6	8	7	3	2
3	6	2	7	9	4	1	5	8
8	5	7	1	2	3	6	9	4

Solutions

370.

5	6	1	8	2	9	3	7	4
9	8	7	3	4	1	6	2	5
2	4	3	5	6	7	8	9	1
8	3	5	4	9	2	1	6	7
6	1	9	7	5	8	4	3	2
4	7	2	6	1	3	5	8	9
3	5	8	9	7	4	2	1	6
7	2	4	1	8	6	9	5	3
1	9	6	2	3	5	7	4	8

371.

7	5	9	8	4	1	3	2	6
3	8	1	9	2	6	7	5	4
2	6	4	3	7	5	1	9	8
5	7	3	4	9	2	8	6	1
9	1	8	6	3	7	2	4	5
6	4	2	5	1	8	9	7	3
8	2	7	1	6	4	5	3	9
4	3	5	7	8	9	6	1	2
1	9	6	2	5	3	4	8	7

372.

4	1	2	6	3	7	5	9	8
5	6	9	4	2	8	3	7	1
8	3	7	1	5	9	6	2	4
2	7	4	5	1	3	9	8	6
6	5	8	9	4	2	7	1	3
1	9	3	8	7	6	2	4	5
9	8	1	2	6	5	4	3	7
3	2	5	7	8	4	1	6	9
7	4	6	3	9	1	8	5	2

373.

8	4	7	6	9	1	3	5	2
2	6	1	5	3	8	4	7	9
3	5	9	4	2	7	1	6	8
5	2	8	7	6	3	9	1	4
7	9	4	1	8	5	2	3	6
1	3	6	2	4	9	7	8	5
9	8	2	3	1	6	5	4	7
6	1	5	9	7	4	8	2	3
4	7	3	8	5	2	6	9	1

374.

8	6	4	9	2	5	1	3	7
9	3	5	7	1	8	2	4	6
7	2	1	3	4	6	9	8	5
1	4	8	6	5	3	7	2	9
6	5	7	2	9	4	3	1	8
3	9	2	8	7	1	5	6	4
5	7	3	4	8	2	6	9	1
2	8	9	1	6	7	4	5	3
4	1	6	5	3	9	8	7	2

375.

2	8	6	1	4	3	7	5	9
7	3	5	6	8	9	4	1	2
9	4	1	5	7	2	6	8	3
5	9	3	4	2	1	8	6	7
4	6	2	8	9	7	1	3	5
8	1	7	3	5	6	9	2	4
6	5	8	7	3	4	2	9	1
3	2	4	9	1	8	5	7	6
1	7	9	2	6	5	3	4	8

376.

8	9	3	4	2	5	1	7	6
4	2	5	6	1	7	9	8	3
7	6	1	3	9	8	2	5	4
5	1	9	2	3	6	7	4	8
6	4	2	7	8	9	3	1	5
3	8	7	5	4	1	6	2	9
2	7	4	9	5	3	8	6	1
1	3	6	8	7	4	5	9	2
9	5	8	1	6	2	4	3	7

377.

7	8	2	5	3	6	9	1	4
6	4	5	8	9	1	3	7	2
1	9	3	7	2	4	5	6	8
4	2	6	3	7	5	8	9	1
3	1	8	9	6	2	7	4	5
9	5	7	1	4	8	2	3	6
2	7	4	6	8	3	1	5	9
5	6	9	2	1	7	4	8	3
8	3	1	4	5	9	6	2	7

378.

7	4	8	3	1	2	9	6	5
3	1	6	7	5	9	8	2	4
5	2	9	6	4	8	1	7	3
8	5	7	1	2	4	6	3	9
1	6	3	5	9	7	2	4	8
4	9	2	8	6	3	7	5	1
2	7	1	4	8	5	3	9	6
6	3	5	9	7	1	4	8	2
9	8	4	2	3	6	5	1	7

Solutions

379.

4	2	3	6	5	9	8	7	1
9	7	1	8	3	4	5	2	6
6	5	8	2	7	1	9	4	3
2	4	5	1	6	7	3	8	9
3	6	7	4	9	8	2	1	5
1	8	9	3	2	5	7	6	4
7	3	2	5	4	6	1	9	8
5	1	6	9	8	2	4	3	7
8	9	4	7	1	3	6	5	2

380.

2	4	5	6	7	9	1	8	3
8	1	7	2	5	3	4	9	6
6	3	9	4	8	1	5	2	7
7	5	3	9	1	6	8	4	2
9	8	1	7	2	4	3	6	5
4	2	6	8	3	5	9	7	1
5	9	8	1	6	7	2	3	4
1	7	4	3	9	2	6	5	8
3	6	2	5	4	8	7	1	9

381.

5	6	9	7	2	1	4	8	3
4	2	1	9	3	8	6	7	5
7	8	3	6	4	5	9	1	2
6	9	7	8	5	2	3	4	1
3	4	2	1	6	7	5	9	8
1	5	8	4	9	3	7	2	6
8	3	5	2	7	4	1	6	9
2	7	6	5	1	9	8	3	4
9	1	4	3	8	6	2	5	7

382.

6	2	7	4	8	1	3	9	5
1	8	3	5	9	6	4	2	7
5	9	4	3	2	7	1	6	8
2	7	9	1	4	3	5	8	6
3	6	8	2	7	5	9	1	4
4	5	1	9	6	8	7	3	2
8	1	2	7	3	4	6	5	9
9	4	5	6	1	2	8	7	3
7	3	6	8	5	9	2	4	1

383.

2	4	3	7	5	8	6	9	1
9	6	5	4	1	2	7	8	3
7	8	1	9	6	3	2	4	5
1	2	7	3	8	6	9	5	4
5	3	6	1	4	9	8	7	2
4	9	8	2	7	5	1	3	6
6	1	4	8	3	7	5	2	9
3	7	9	5	2	1	4	6	8
8	5	2	6	9	4	3	1	7

384.

9	2	1	5	7	6	4	3	8
5	7	4	3	2	8	1	9	6
8	6	3	1	9	4	5	7	2
1	5	2	6	4	3	7	8	9
6	4	9	7	8	1	3	2	5
7	3	8	2	5	9	6	4	1
3	9	5	4	1	2	8	6	7
2	1	6	8	3	7	9	5	4
4	8	7	9	6	5	2	1	3

385.

2	4	5	3	7	8	9	1	6
8	9	3	5	6	1	7	4	2
1	6	7	2	4	9	5	3	8
6	5	8	1	3	4	2	9	7
7	2	4	9	8	5	3	6	1
9	3	1	6	2	7	4	8	5
4	7	9	8	1	2	6	5	3
5	8	6	7	9	3	1	2	4
3	1	2	4	5	6	8	7	9

386.

5	7	3	9	4	2	8	6	1
4	9	8	1	3	6	2	5	7
6	1	2	8	5	7	4	9	3
7	4	9	2	6	1	3	8	5
1	3	5	4	7	8	9	2	6
8	2	6	3	9	5	1	7	4
3	8	7	6	2	4	5	1	9
2	6	4	5	1	9	7	3	8
9	5	1	7	8	3	6	4	2

387.

8	3	9	6	7	4	1	2	5
7	6	1	5	3	2	4	9	8
4	5	2	9	8	1	7	6	3
5	4	7	1	9	3	2	8	6
3	2	6	4	5	8	9	1	7
1	9	8	2	6	7	5	3	4
2	8	3	7	1	5	6	4	9
9	1	5	8	4	6	3	7	2
6	7	4	3	2	9	8	5	1

Solutions

388.

9	5	1	3	4	8	6	7	2
4	2	6	7	9	1	3	5	8
8	3	7	2	6	5	9	1	4
6	4	9	8	1	7	2	3	5
1	8	5	9	3	2	4	6	7
2	7	3	6	5	4	8	9	1
7	9	2	1	8	3	5	4	6
3	1	4	5	2	6	7	8	9
5	6	8	4	7	9	1	2	3

389.

9	6	4	8	2	7	5	1	3
3	7	1	5	6	4	2	9	8
2	8	5	3	1	9	6	7	4
1	2	6	9	4	8	7	3	5
8	3	9	6	7	5	1	4	2
5	4	7	2	3	1	8	6	9
7	5	8	1	9	3	4	2	6
4	9	2	7	5	6	3	8	1
6	1	3	4	8	2	9	5	7

390.

2	7	6	5	9	4	8	1	3
1	9	3	8	6	2	5	7	4
4	5	8	3	1	7	6	2	9
7	8	4	1	2	5	3	9	6
9	6	5	4	7	3	1	8	2
3	2	1	9	8	6	7	4	5
5	1	9	6	4	8	2	3	7
8	3	7	2	5	9	4	6	1
6	4	2	7	3	1	9	5	8

391.

6	8	1	9	3	5	4	7	2
7	4	5	8	1	2	6	3	9
9	3	2	7	4	6	1	5	8
4	7	6	3	5	9	8	2	1
2	5	8	1	7	4	9	6	3
1	9	3	6	2	8	7	4	5
3	6	7	5	9	1	2	8	4
8	2	9	4	6	3	5	1	7
5	1	4	2	8	7	3	9	6

392.

2	9	5	1	7	3	6	8	4
8	6	4	2	5	9	3	1	7
1	3	7	6	8	4	5	2	9
3	7	1	4	6	2	9	5	8
4	5	9	8	3	1	2	7	6
6	2	8	5	9	7	4	3	1
5	8	3	7	4	6	1	9	2
9	1	6	3	2	8	7	4	5
7	4	2	9	1	5	8	6	3

393.

3	5	2	9	1	8	4	6	7
8	9	1	4	6	7	2	3	5
4	6	7	2	5	3	1	8	9
5	7	3	1	4	2	6	9	8
6	8	4	5	7	9	3	2	1
2	1	9	8	3	6	5	7	4
1	3	8	7	2	5	9	4	6
7	2	5	6	9	4	8	1	3
9	4	6	3	8	1	7	5	2

394.

4	2	1	3	9	5	7	6	8
5	7	8	6	2	4	9	1	3
6	3	9	7	8	1	2	5	4
9	5	2	1	7	8	3	4	6
8	4	3	5	6	2	1	9	7
1	6	7	9	4	3	8	2	5
2	8	6	4	1	7	5	3	9
7	9	5	2	3	6	4	8	1
3	1	4	8	5	9	6	7	2

395.

3	7	6	1	5	2	9	4	8
2	1	4	6	9	8	7	3	5
8	9	5	7	3	4	2	1	6
5	6	1	2	7	9	3	8	4
4	2	3	8	1	6	5	7	9
9	8	7	5	4	3	1	6	2
1	3	9	4	6	5	8	2	7
7	4	2	9	8	1	6	5	3
6	5	8	3	2	7	4	9	1

396.

8	1	7	5	2	6	4	9	3
6	9	3	1	8	4	2	7	5
5	4	2	9	7	3	8	1	6
9	2	1	3	6	5	7	8	4
3	5	4	8	1	7	9	6	2
7	6	8	2	4	9	3	5	1
2	3	5	7	9	1	6	4	8
1	7	6	4	3	8	5	2	9
4	8	9	6	5	2	1	3	7

Solutions

397.

1	6	7	2	9	3	5	8	4
4	5	3	1	6	8	2	7	9
2	8	9	7	5	4	3	6	1
9	3	6	4	8	2	7	1	5
8	1	4	5	3	7	9	2	6
7	2	5	9	1	6	8	4	3
3	4	2	6	7	9	1	5	8
5	7	8	3	4	1	6	9	2
6	9	1	8	2	5	4	3	7

398.

3	1	6	2	8	4	5	9	7
7	2	5	3	6	9	4	8	1
8	4	9	7	1	5	6	2	3
4	3	1	8	2	6	9	7	5
5	6	7	9	4	1	8	3	2
9	8	2	5	7	3	1	4	6
6	5	8	4	3	7	2	1	9
1	7	4	6	9	2	3	5	8
2	9	3	1	5	8	7	6	4

399.

9	2	6	8	5	4	1	3	7
1	7	5	3	9	2	8	4	6
4	8	3	6	1	7	9	5	2
7	3	4	2	8	6	5	9	1
8	9	2	5	7	1	4	6	3
6	5	1	4	3	9	7	2	8
2	6	8	1	4	5	3	7	9
3	4	7	9	2	8	6	1	5
5	1	9	7	6	3	2	8	4

400.

2	6	9	4	3	7	1	8	5
5	8	4	6	2	1	3	7	9
7	3	1	8	5	9	6	2	4
8	4	5	3	1	6	2	9	7
1	9	6	2	7	4	5	3	8
3	7	2	5	9	8	4	6	1
6	1	7	9	4	3	8	5	2
9	2	8	1	6	5	7	4	3
4	5	3	7	8	2	9	1	6

401.

1	5	6	7	3	4	8	2	9
7	4	9	8	2	1	5	3	6
2	8	3	5	9	6	7	4	1
4	7	8	6	1	9	2	5	3
5	3	1	4	7	2	9	6	8
6	9	2	3	5	8	4	1	7
9	2	4	1	6	7	3	8	5
8	6	5	9	4	3	1	7	2
3	1	7	2	8	5	6	9	4

402.

9	3	4	6	8	7	5	2	1
5	1	7	2	9	3	6	4	8
8	6	2	4	5	1	3	9	7
7	4	3	1	2	5	8	6	9
2	8	5	3	6	9	7	1	4
6	9	1	7	4	8	2	3	5
1	5	9	8	3	6	4	7	2
3	2	8	9	7	4	1	5	6
4	7	6	5	1	2	9	8	3

403.

1	8	2	6	5	4	3	9	7
9	6	7	2	3	8	1	5	4
5	3	4	7	9	1	8	2	6
3	9	6	1	8	2	7	4	5
4	1	5	3	7	9	2	6	8
7	2	8	4	6	5	9	3	1
2	7	1	9	4	6	5	8	3
6	5	3	8	2	7	4	1	9
8	4	9	5	1	3	6	7	2

404.

2	6	4	3	7	9	1	8	5
3	8	9	1	5	4	6	7	2
5	1	7	2	8	6	4	3	9
6	4	2	5	9	7	3	1	8
1	9	5	6	3	8	2	4	7
7	3	8	4	2	1	9	5	6
9	5	3	7	4	2	8	6	1
4	2	1	8	6	5	7	9	3
8	7	6	9	1	3	5	2	4

405.

8	5	6	4	9	2	3	1	7
7	9	1	3	8	6	4	2	5
4	2	3	1	5	7	6	8	9
3	4	9	7	1	8	5	6	2
6	7	8	2	3	5	1	9	4
5	1	2	9	6	4	8	7	3
9	8	5	6	2	3	7	4	1
2	6	7	5	4	1	9	3	8
1	3	4	8	7	9	2	5	6

Solutions

406.

8	2	1	7	5	9	4	6	3
9	4	3	6	2	1	5	7	8
5	7	6	8	3	4	2	1	9
1	8	4	2	9	6	7	3	5
2	3	7	5	1	8	9	4	6
6	9	5	4	7	3	8	2	1
4	1	9	3	8	7	6	5	2
7	5	8	1	6	2	3	9	4
3	6	2	9	4	5	1	8	7

407.

7	5	6	9	4	3	1	8	2
9	2	1	6	7	8	5	3	4
4	3	8	5	1	2	6	9	7
3	4	5	2	8	9	7	6	1
8	1	7	4	3	6	2	5	9
6	9	2	7	5	1	3	4	8
5	6	9	1	2	4	8	7	3
2	8	4	3	6	7	9	1	5
1	7	3	8	9	5	4	2	6

408.

4	8	6	3	5	2	9	1	7
1	7	3	8	9	4	2	5	6
5	2	9	7	6	1	3	8	4
6	4	8	1	2	3	5	7	9
9	1	7	4	8	5	6	3	2
3	5	2	9	7	6	8	4	1
2	3	4	5	1	9	7	6	8
7	9	1	6	3	8	4	2	5
8	6	5	2	4	7	1	9	3

409.

4	1	3	2	7	9	6	8	5
2	9	8	3	5	6	4	7	1
6	5	7	8	1	4	2	9	3
8	7	2	5	9	3	1	6	4
5	3	6	1	4	8	7	2	9
1	4	9	7	6	2	5	3	8
9	2	4	6	8	5	3	1	7
3	8	1	4	2	7	9	5	6
7	6	5	9	3	1	8	4	2

410.

8	6	2	3	4	1	5	9	7
3	9	5	8	7	2	1	4	6
7	4	1	9	5	6	3	8	2
4	1	6	5	9	8	2	7	3
9	5	3	2	6	7	8	1	4
2	8	7	4	1	3	9	6	5
1	3	8	6	2	4	7	5	9
6	7	9	1	3	5	4	2	8
5	2	4	7	8	9	6	3	1

411.

5	1	3	6	7	9	4	8	2
2	8	6	1	5	4	7	9	3
9	4	7	3	2	8	5	1	6
1	6	5	9	8	3	2	4	7
3	7	8	2	4	6	9	5	1
4	9	2	5	1	7	6	3	8
7	3	1	4	9	2	8	6	5
8	5	4	7	6	1	3	2	9
6	2	9	8	3	5	1	7	4

412.

7	8	9	2	1	3	6	4	5
2	5	6	9	4	8	3	7	1
4	1	3	5	7	6	9	8	2
9	4	8	3	2	1	7	5	6
3	2	1	7	6	5	8	9	4
5	6	7	8	9	4	1	2	3
8	9	4	1	3	2	5	6	7
1	7	2	6	5	9	4	3	8
6	3	5	4	8	7	2	1	9

413.

4	2	8	7	6	3	1	5	9
3	5	7	1	8	9	4	6	2
6	9	1	4	2	5	8	3	7
1	3	4	5	7	8	9	2	6
8	7	9	2	1	6	5	4	3
5	6	2	9	3	4	7	1	8
7	4	5	3	9	2	6	8	1
9	8	3	6	4	1	2	7	5
2	1	6	8	5	7	3	9	4

414.

5	3	9	4	2	6	7	8	1
4	2	7	9	8	1	6	5	3
1	6	8	3	7	5	2	9	4
9	4	3	8	5	2	1	6	7
7	5	6	1	3	9	8	4	2
8	1	2	6	4	7	5	3	9
6	7	5	2	9	4	3	1	8
2	8	4	5	1	3	9	7	6
3	9	1	7	6	8	4	2	5

415.

5	1	6	3	9	7	2	4	8
2	3	7	4	5	8	1	6	9
8	4	9	1	6	2	5	3	7
9	2	5	8	7	4	6	1	3
3	6	4	9	2	1	7	8	5
7	8	1	6	3	5	4	9	2
6	7	8	5	4	3	9	2	1
1	9	2	7	8	6	3	5	4
4	5	3	2	1	9	8	7	6

416.

5	8	4	7	1	3	6	9	2
3	6	1	2	8	9	7	5	4
2	7	9	4	5	6	8	1	3
6	4	5	1	2	7	3	8	9
9	3	2	5	6	8	1	4	7
8	1	7	9	3	4	2	6	5
4	2	8	6	7	5	9	3	1
7	9	6	3	4	1	5	2	8
1	5	3	8	9	2	4	7	6

417.

3	2	1	9	6	7	4	8	5
7	4	6	1	5	8	9	2	3
9	5	8	3	2	4	1	7	6
5	9	2	8	3	1	7	6	4
6	1	4	5	7	2	3	9	8
8	7	3	4	9	6	2	5	1
4	8	9	7	1	5	6	3	2
1	6	7	2	8	3	5	4	9
2	3	5	6	4	9	8	1	7

418.

1	5	3	9	2	6	7	4	8
9	2	7	4	8	1	6	5	3
4	8	6	7	3	5	1	9	2
6	1	4	3	9	7	2	8	5
2	3	8	5	6	4	9	7	1
7	9	5	2	1	8	3	6	4
8	7	1	6	5	2	4	3	9
3	4	2	8	7	9	5	1	6
5	6	9	1	4	3	8	2	7

419.

2	1	6	3	9	5	8	4	7
5	4	3	7	8	1	2	6	9
9	7	8	2	6	4	3	1	5
1	9	5	6	3	8	7	2	4
4	8	2	1	7	9	6	5	3
6	3	7	4	5	2	1	9	8
8	2	4	9	1	7	5	3	6
3	5	1	8	4	6	9	7	2
7	6	9	5	2	3	4	8	1

420.

1	5	4	8	3	9	6	7	2
2	6	8	1	4	7	9	5	3
7	9	3	2	5	6	4	8	1
3	1	7	6	9	5	8	2	4
8	2	5	3	1	4	7	9	6
6	4	9	7	2	8	1	3	5
4	8	6	5	7	3	2	1	9
5	7	1	9	6	2	3	4	8
9	3	2	4	8	1	5	6	7

421.

1	7	6	5	2	4	8	3	9
3	4	5	7	9	8	2	6	1
8	9	2	1	3	6	7	5	4
9	2	8	4	5	7	6	1	3
4	5	1	2	6	3	9	7	8
7	6	3	8	1	9	5	4	2
2	1	7	3	8	5	4	9	6
5	8	9	6	4	1	3	2	7
6	3	4	9	7	2	1	8	5

422.

4	3	8	2	1	9	5	7	6
6	2	7	4	3	5	1	9	8
9	1	5	6	7	8	3	4	2
7	6	2	8	9	1	4	5	3
5	9	1	3	4	2	8	6	7
8	4	3	5	6	7	2	1	9
2	5	6	7	8	4	9	3	1
1	7	4	9	2	3	6	8	5
3	8	9	1	5	6	7	2	4

423.

8	4	5	1	7	9	2	3	6
2	1	6	8	3	5	4	7	9
3	9	7	4	6	2	1	8	5
6	5	8	7	1	3	9	2	4
4	2	3	6	9	8	7	5	1
9	7	1	5	2	4	8	6	3
5	6	2	9	4	7	3	1	8
7	8	9	3	5	1	6	4	2
1	3	4	2	8	6	5	9	7

Solutions

424.

8	4	7	3	2	5	6	1	9
2	9	3	1	6	4	7	5	8
6	1	5	9	8	7	3	2	4
3	2	9	5	1	8	4	7	6
7	8	1	6	4	3	2	9	5
4	5	6	7	9	2	1	8	3
1	3	2	4	5	9	8	6	7
5	6	4	8	7	1	9	3	2
9	7	8	2	3	6	5	4	1

425.

3	6	1	4	2	8	7	5	9
7	5	9	3	1	6	8	4	2
2	4	8	7	5	9	3	1	6
8	9	4	2	6	1	5	7	3
5	2	3	9	8	7	4	6	1
1	7	6	5	3	4	9	2	8
9	3	5	6	4	2	1	8	7
4	8	2	1	7	3	6	9	5
6	1	7	8	9	5	2	3	4

426.

7	9	1	8	3	6	5	4	2
5	3	6	4	2	9	8	1	7
2	8	4	1	7	5	9	3	6
1	5	3	7	6	4	2	8	9
8	4	7	2	9	1	3	6	5
6	2	9	5	8	3	4	7	1
3	1	5	6	4	2	7	9	8
9	6	8	3	5	7	1	2	4
4	7	2	9	1	8	6	5	3

427.

8	9	7	3	4	6	5	1	2
5	1	3	7	2	9	6	8	4
6	4	2	1	5	8	3	7	9
4	7	8	6	9	1	2	5	3
1	3	9	5	7	2	4	6	8
2	5	6	4	8	3	1	9	7
9	8	4	2	6	5	7	3	1
7	6	1	8	3	4	9	2	5
3	2	5	9	1	7	8	4	6

428.

8	6	4	1	5	9	7	3	2
1	5	7	2	3	4	6	9	8
2	9	3	7	6	8	1	5	4
4	1	2	8	7	5	3	6	9
9	3	5	6	4	1	8	2	7
7	8	6	3	9	2	5	4	1
3	4	8	9	1	6	2	7	5
6	2	9	5	8	7	4	1	3
5	7	1	4	2	3	9	8	6

429.

5	3	2	7	8	4	1	6	9
4	6	7	2	9	1	5	3	8
9	1	8	3	5	6	7	2	4
6	4	5	8	2	9	3	1	7
7	8	1	6	3	5	4	9	2
2	9	3	1	4	7	6	8	5
1	7	9	4	6	8	2	5	3
8	2	6	5	7	3	9	4	1
3	5	4	9	1	2	8	7	6

430.

8	2	4	3	5	7	1	6	9
7	5	9	1	6	2	3	4	8
3	1	6	9	4	8	5	2	7
9	8	5	6	2	4	7	3	1
1	7	2	5	8	3	6	9	4
6	4	3	7	9	1	8	5	2
4	9	7	8	3	5	2	1	6
5	6	1	2	7	9	4	8	3
2	3	8	4	1	6	9	7	5

431.

9	3	5	6	2	8	7	1	4
4	8	1	7	9	3	5	2	6
7	2	6	5	4	1	8	9	3
6	1	2	8	7	9	3	4	5
8	9	3	4	6	5	2	7	1
5	4	7	3	1	2	9	6	8
3	7	9	1	8	6	4	5	2
2	6	8	9	5	4	1	3	7
1	5	4	2	3	7	6	8	9

432.

7	5	3	9	6	2	8	4	1
1	2	9	5	4	8	3	6	7
4	8	6	1	3	7	5	2	9
8	7	4	6	1	3	2	9	5
9	6	2	8	5	4	7	1	3
5	3	1	2	7	9	4	8	6
6	4	7	3	2	1	9	5	8
3	1	8	4	9	5	6	7	2
2	9	5	7	8	6	1	3	4

433.

5	2	1	7	4	9	8	6	3
7	3	9	8	6	5	2	1	4
4	6	8	3	2	1	9	7	5
1	7	3	9	8	4	6	5	2
9	4	5	6	7	2	1	3	8
2	8	6	5	1	3	4	9	7
8	9	2	1	3	7	5	4	6
3	5	4	2	9	6	7	8	1
6	1	7	4	5	8	3	2	9

434.

5	2	4	1	9	3	6	8	7
8	9	3	6	7	4	1	2	5
7	1	6	5	2	8	4	9	3
2	5	8	7	4	6	3	1	9
4	7	9	2	3	1	8	5	6
6	3	1	8	5	9	2	7	4
3	6	2	9	1	7	5	4	8
1	8	7	4	6	5	9	3	2
9	4	5	3	8	2	7	6	1

435.

6	1	4	9	5	7	3	8	2
2	7	8	3	6	1	5	9	4
3	5	9	4	2	8	7	1	6
7	2	1	5	8	6	4	3	9
9	3	5	7	1	4	6	2	8
4	8	6	2	3	9	1	5	7
1	9	2	6	7	5	8	4	3
5	6	3	8	4	2	9	7	1
8	4	7	1	9	3	2	6	5

436.

7	8	3	5	4	2	6	9	1
2	9	4	1	3	6	5	8	7
6	5	1	9	8	7	4	3	2
3	6	5	7	2	9	8	1	4
8	4	2	3	5	1	9	7	6
1	7	9	8	6	4	2	5	3
4	1	8	2	9	3	7	6	5
5	2	7	6	1	8	3	4	9
9	3	6	4	7	5	1	2	8

437.

8	2	7	5	4	1	3	6	9
6	4	9	3	7	8	5	2	1
1	5	3	2	9	6	8	7	4
3	1	2	9	5	7	4	8	6
4	7	6	1	8	2	9	3	5
5	9	8	6	3	4	2	1	7
7	3	4	8	6	9	1	5	2
9	8	1	7	2	5	6	4	3
2	6	5	4	1	3	7	9	8

438.

9	8	1	5	3	6	4	7	2
4	2	5	7	1	8	9	6	3
6	7	3	2	9	4	5	1	8
8	1	9	3	6	5	2	4	7
2	5	4	8	7	1	6	3	9
7	3	6	4	2	9	8	5	1
5	6	7	1	8	2	3	9	4
1	9	8	6	4	3	7	2	5
3	4	2	9	5	7	1	8	6

439.

6	8	7	1	9	5	2	3	4
4	3	9	6	2	8	1	5	7
5	1	2	7	3	4	6	9	8
2	7	3	9	8	1	4	6	5
1	6	8	5	4	3	7	2	9
9	4	5	2	6	7	8	1	3
3	5	4	8	1	6	9	7	2
7	2	1	4	5	9	3	8	6
8	9	6	3	7	2	5	4	1

440.

4	7	9	8	5	2	1	3	6
2	3	5	9	6	1	8	4	7
1	8	6	3	7	4	5	9	2
9	4	8	7	1	5	6	2	3
7	5	2	4	3	6	9	1	8
6	1	3	2	8	9	4	7	5
8	2	1	5	9	3	7	6	4
3	6	7	1	4	8	2	5	9
5	9	4	6	2	7	3	8	1

441.

7	8	9	3	1	5	4	2	6
3	1	2	6	8	4	5	9	7
4	6	5	2	9	7	3	8	1
2	3	6	9	4	1	8	7	5
5	4	8	7	3	2	6	1	9
9	7	1	8	5	6	2	4	3
1	9	3	4	6	8	7	5	2
6	2	4	5	7	9	1	3	8
8	5	7	1	2	3	9	6	4

Solutions

442.

8	5	6	3	4	2	1	7	9
7	3	2	9	1	8	6	5	4
1	9	4	7	6	5	2	3	8
3	2	9	8	5	6	4	1	7
5	1	8	2	7	4	9	6	3
6	4	7	1	9	3	5	8	2
9	7	3	5	2	1	8	4	6
2	6	5	4	8	7	3	9	1
4	8	1	6	3	9	7	2	5

443.

8	9	2	7	1	4	5	3	6
6	3	5	9	2	8	7	1	4
4	1	7	6	5	3	8	9	2
9	8	3	2	6	5	1	4	7
5	4	1	3	8	7	2	6	9
2	7	6	1	4	9	3	8	5
1	5	8	4	9	2	6	7	3
7	6	9	5	3	1	4	2	8
3	2	4	8	7	6	9	5	1

444.

2	6	3	8	4	9	7	5	1
8	9	7	2	5	1	4	3	6
4	5	1	7	6	3	9	2	8
7	2	5	4	3	8	6	1	9
1	8	6	9	7	5	2	4	3
3	4	9	6	1	2	8	7	5
6	3	4	1	9	7	5	8	2
9	1	8	5	2	4	3	6	7
5	7	2	3	8	6	1	9	4

445.

4	8	6	1	5	3	9	7	2
3	9	2	7	4	6	1	8	5
1	5	7	2	8	9	4	3	6
2	4	8	6	3	5	7	9	1
5	7	1	9	2	4	3	6	8
6	3	9	8	7	1	5	2	4
8	1	3	5	6	7	2	4	9
7	6	5	4	9	2	8	1	3
9	2	4	3	1	8	6	5	7

446.

5	3	9	6	2	1	4	7	8
4	1	8	5	3	7	9	6	2
6	2	7	9	4	8	3	1	5
2	6	4	1	5	3	7	8	9
7	9	3	2	8	6	5	4	1
1	8	5	4	7	9	6	2	3
9	5	1	7	6	2	8	3	4
3	4	6	8	1	5	2	9	7
8	7	2	3	9	4	1	5	6

447.

3	7	2	6	9	1	5	4	8
9	1	6	5	8	4	3	7	2
5	4	8	7	3	2	6	9	1
4	2	5	3	6	7	8	1	9
8	3	9	1	4	5	7	2	6
1	6	7	9	2	8	4	3	5
6	8	1	4	7	9	2	5	3
2	9	4	8	5	3	1	6	7
7	5	3	2	1	6	9	8	4

448.

2	1	7	4	6	5	3	9	8
8	5	6	2	3	9	1	7	4
3	4	9	7	1	8	2	5	6
6	9	3	1	8	2	5	4	7
1	7	4	5	9	6	8	3	2
5	8	2	3	4	7	9	6	1
9	2	8	6	5	4	7	1	3
4	3	5	8	7	1	6	2	9
7	6	1	9	2	3	4	8	5

449.

4	6	8	9	3	2	7	1	5
1	3	2	8	7	5	4	6	9
7	5	9	4	1	6	2	8	3
5	2	6	3	9	8	1	7	4
3	9	1	7	2	4	8	5	6
8	7	4	6	5	1	3	9	2
2	8	5	1	6	3	9	4	7
6	1	7	2	4	9	5	3	8
9	4	3	5	8	7	6	2	1

450.

9	8	7	6	2	3	1	5	4
4	1	6	8	5	9	3	2	7
2	3	5	1	4	7	8	9	6
6	9	3	4	1	8	5	7	2
7	5	8	3	6	2	9	4	1
1	2	4	7	9	5	6	3	8
5	4	2	9	8	1	7	6	3
3	6	1	5	7	4	2	8	9
8	7	9	2	3	6	4	1	5

451.

1	5	4	3	9	2	8	7	6
6	9	7	1	8	5	2	4	3
3	2	8	4	6	7	9	5	1
9	3	5	6	7	4	1	2	8
2	7	6	8	5	1	3	9	4
8	4	1	9	2	3	5	6	7
4	1	9	5	3	6	7	8	2
5	6	2	7	1	8	4	3	9
7	8	3	2	4	9	6	1	5

452.

2	7	6	3	8	5	4	1	9
3	1	5	9	4	6	7	2	8
8	4	9	2	1	7	3	6	5
5	2	3	7	9	8	6	4	1
7	9	1	6	2	4	8	5	3
6	8	4	1	5	3	2	9	7
1	6	8	5	3	2	9	7	4
4	5	7	8	6	9	1	3	2
9	3	2	4	7	1	5	8	6

453.

9	2	8	7	5	6	3	4	1
1	7	3	2	4	8	9	5	6
5	4	6	3	1	9	8	2	7
7	3	5	6	9	2	4	1	8
8	6	2	4	7	1	5	3	9
4	1	9	8	3	5	6	7	2
2	5	4	9	8	7	1	6	3
3	9	7	1	6	4	2	8	5
6	8	1	5	2	3	7	9	4

454.

7	2	9	6	8	5	1	4	3
4	6	5	3	1	2	7	8	9
3	8	1	4	7	9	2	6	5
6	5	4	8	3	7	9	1	2
2	3	8	5	9	1	4	7	6
1	9	7	2	4	6	3	5	8
9	7	6	1	2	8	5	3	4
5	4	2	7	6	3	8	9	1
8	1	3	9	5	4	6	2	7

455.

8	1	5	2	7	9	3	4	6
3	7	9	6	4	8	5	2	1
2	6	4	1	3	5	9	8	7
6	9	3	5	8	7	2	1	4
1	2	8	4	9	6	7	3	5
4	5	7	3	1	2	8	6	9
9	4	2	8	5	1	6	7	3
5	3	6	7	2	4	1	9	8
7	8	1	9	6	3	4	5	2

456.

6	7	5	4	1	8	2	9	3
2	8	9	7	3	5	4	6	1
3	4	1	2	6	9	5	8	7
4	2	6	8	5	3	7	1	9
5	9	3	1	2	7	6	4	8
7	1	8	9	4	6	3	5	2
8	6	4	3	9	2	1	7	5
9	5	2	6	7	1	8	3	4
1	3	7	5	8	4	9	2	6

457.

7	3	8	1	4	5	6	9	2
4	9	1	2	3	6	8	7	5
6	5	2	8	9	7	1	3	4
9	6	7	3	8	4	2	5	1
1	8	3	9	5	2	7	4	6
2	4	5	6	7	1	3	8	9
8	1	4	5	6	3	9	2	7
5	2	9	7	1	8	4	6	3
3	7	6	4	2	9	5	1	8

458.

2	1	3	8	4	6	5	9	7
5	4	9	1	7	2	6	8	3
8	6	7	9	3	5	1	4	2
3	9	5	2	1	4	8	7	6
4	7	2	5	6	8	9	3	1
1	8	6	7	9	3	4	2	5
6	5	4	3	8	7	2	1	9
7	2	1	4	5	9	3	6	8
9	3	8	6	2	1	7	5	4

459.

7	2	5	4	3	8	1	9	6
8	4	6	9	1	7	2	3	5
1	9	3	2	6	5	8	7	4
4	7	2	8	5	9	6	1	3
3	5	9	1	4	6	7	8	2
6	1	8	7	2	3	5	4	9
2	3	4	6	7	1	9	5	8
9	6	1	5	8	4	3	2	7
5	8	7	3	9	2	4	6	1

Solutions

460.

8	4	6	2	9	7	3	1	5
9	1	3	6	5	4	7	8	2
2	7	5	8	1	3	9	4	6
7	9	4	3	2	1	6	5	8
1	5	2	9	6	8	4	7	3
6	3	8	4	7	5	1	2	9
3	8	7	5	4	6	2	9	1
4	6	9	1	8	2	5	3	7
5	2	1	7	3	9	8	6	4

461.

3	8	6	7	5	2	1	4	9
7	1	9	4	8	6	5	3	2
2	4	5	1	9	3	6	7	8
5	7	8	2	4	9	3	1	6
9	2	4	6	3	1	7	8	5
6	3	1	8	7	5	2	9	4
1	5	7	9	2	8	4	6	3
8	6	2	3	1	4	9	5	7
4	9	3	5	6	7	8	2	1

462.

9	2	8	7	3	1	4	5	6
6	1	5	4	2	8	3	7	9
7	4	3	9	6	5	1	2	8
8	9	1	6	7	4	2	3	5
5	7	4	2	8	3	6	9	1
3	6	2	1	5	9	8	4	7
1	8	7	5	4	2	9	6	3
4	3	6	8	9	7	5	1	2
2	5	9	3	1	6	7	8	4

463.

1	5	9	7	3	2	8	6	4
3	4	2	8	6	5	1	9	7
8	6	7	1	9	4	2	3	5
7	3	6	5	2	1	9	4	8
2	9	4	6	8	3	7	5	1
5	1	8	9	4	7	3	2	6
4	7	5	2	1	9	6	8	3
9	8	1	3	5	6	4	7	2
6	2	3	4	7	8	5	1	9

464.

4	6	8	9	5	3	2	1	7
2	5	1	4	7	8	3	6	9
3	7	9	6	2	1	8	5	4
9	4	7	2	6	5	1	3	8
8	2	5	3	1	9	7	4	6
1	3	6	8	4	7	5	9	2
7	8	3	5	9	6	4	2	1
6	1	2	7	3	4	9	8	5
5	9	4	1	8	2	6	7	3

465.

7	1	9	2	5	6	4	8	3
2	5	4	7	3	8	1	6	9
6	8	3	9	1	4	5	2	7
8	6	2	3	7	1	9	4	5
4	9	7	6	8	5	2	3	1
1	3	5	4	9	2	6	7	8
9	7	6	5	2	3	8	1	4
5	2	8	1	4	7	3	9	6
3	4	1	8	6	9	7	5	2

466.

2	6	1	4	5	7	3	9	8
5	9	4	1	8	3	7	6	2
8	7	3	9	6	2	5	1	4
3	2	5	6	9	4	1	8	7
7	1	9	5	2	8	6	4	3
4	8	6	3	7	1	9	2	5
1	5	8	2	3	6	4	7	9
6	3	2	7	4	9	8	5	1
9	4	7	8	1	5	2	3	6

467.

7	3	4	8	5	2	9	6	1
5	8	1	6	9	7	2	3	4
6	9	2	4	1	3	8	7	5
1	7	8	5	2	6	3	4	9
4	6	3	9	7	1	5	2	8
9	2	5	3	8	4	7	1	6
2	1	9	7	6	8	4	5	3
8	4	7	1	3	5	6	9	2
3	5	6	2	4	9	1	8	7

468.

5	2	7	6	8	3	9	4	1
6	4	3	1	7	9	5	2	8
9	1	8	4	5	2	7	6	3
8	9	5	2	6	7	1	3	4
4	3	6	5	9	1	8	7	2
2	7	1	8	3	4	6	9	5
3	8	2	7	1	6	4	5	9
7	5	4	9	2	8	3	1	6
1	6	9	3	4	5	2	8	7

Solutions

469.

9	2	6	5	8	7	4	1	3
4	5	7	2	1	3	8	9	6
3	1	8	6	4	9	2	7	5
5	9	2	8	7	4	6	3	1
6	4	3	9	2	1	5	8	7
7	8	1	3	6	5	9	2	4
2	3	4	1	5	8	7	6	9
1	6	5	7	9	2	3	4	8
8	7	9	4	3	6	1	5	2

470.

7	6	3	2	8	5	1	4	9
5	2	1	4	7	9	8	6	3
9	4	8	1	3	6	7	5	2
8	1	7	5	4	3	2	9	6
3	9	2	6	1	8	4	7	5
6	5	4	9	2	7	3	1	8
1	7	6	8	5	2	9	3	4
4	8	9	3	6	1	5	2	7
2	3	5	7	9	4	6	8	1

471.

7	4	1	2	6	5	3	9	8
3	9	5	1	7	8	2	4	6
2	8	6	3	4	9	1	7	5
1	6	3	8	5	4	9	2	7
8	7	4	6	9	2	5	1	3
9	5	2	7	1	3	6	8	4
5	2	8	9	3	7	4	6	1
4	1	9	5	8	6	7	3	2
6	3	7	4	2	1	8	5	9

472.

8	5	9	2	6	4	7	1	3
3	6	4	1	7	9	5	8	2
2	1	7	3	8	5	6	4	9
1	8	3	4	9	7	2	5	6
6	9	2	8	5	3	1	7	4
4	7	5	6	2	1	9	3	8
5	4	8	9	1	6	3	2	7
9	2	1	7	3	8	4	6	5
7	3	6	5	4	2	8	9	1

473.

9	4	7	3	8	6	2	1	5
8	2	6	1	5	7	4	9	3
5	3	1	9	4	2	7	8	6
3	7	5	8	1	4	6	2	9
2	1	4	6	7	9	3	5	8
6	9	8	2	3	5	1	7	4
7	5	3	4	2	8	9	6	1
4	6	2	5	9	1	8	3	7
1	8	9	7	6	3	5	4	2

474.

8	6	4	5	7	3	2	1	9
1	9	3	8	2	4	5	7	6
5	7	2	1	6	9	4	3	8
6	4	5	9	3	8	1	2	7
3	8	9	7	1	2	6	5	4
7	2	1	6	4	5	9	8	3
2	1	6	4	8	7	3	9	5
9	3	7	2	5	6	8	4	1
4	5	8	3	9	1	7	6	2

475.

7	1	2	6	9	5	3	4	8
9	3	6	2	8	4	5	7	1
5	8	4	7	1	3	9	2	6
3	9	5	8	6	7	2	1	4
2	6	8	4	3	1	7	9	5
1	4	7	5	2	9	6	8	3
6	7	9	1	5	8	4	3	2
8	5	3	9	4	2	1	6	7
4	2	1	3	7	6	8	5	9

476.

7	5	9	4	3	8	6	2	1
6	2	3	9	7	1	8	4	5
4	1	8	6	5	2	9	7	3
1	6	7	8	9	5	4	3	2
3	4	2	7	1	6	5	8	9
9	8	5	2	4	3	1	6	7
8	3	6	1	2	9	7	5	4
2	7	1	5	8	4	3	9	6
5	9	4	3	6	7	2	1	8

477.

4	7	3	9	2	8	6	5	1
6	2	9	1	5	3	7	8	4
8	1	5	7	4	6	3	2	9
1	5	6	2	9	7	4	3	8
2	3	4	6	8	5	1	9	7
9	8	7	3	1	4	2	6	5
5	9	2	4	6	1	8	7	3
3	6	1	8	7	9	5	4	2
7	4	8	5	3	2	9	1	6

Solutions

478.

6	9	2	4	3	7	1	5	8
4	1	8	5	6	2	3	9	7
7	5	3	9	1	8	6	4	2
5	4	1	8	9	6	2	7	3
2	7	9	1	5	3	4	8	6
3	8	6	2	7	4	5	1	9
9	2	4	6	8	5	7	3	1
8	6	7	3	4	1	9	2	5
1	3	5	7	2	9	8	6	4

479.

7	1	4	9	3	8	5	2	6
5	3	2	1	6	7	9	8	4
6	8	9	2	4	5	7	3	1
3	2	1	4	7	6	8	5	9
4	7	8	5	9	2	6	1	3
9	6	5	8	1	3	2	4	7
8	4	6	7	5	1	3	9	2
2	9	7	3	8	4	1	6	5
1	5	3	6	2	9	4	7	8

480.

5	2	4	6	1	3	7	8	9
6	1	9	7	8	5	4	3	2
7	8	3	4	9	2	1	6	5
8	3	7	2	4	1	9	5	6
2	9	1	5	6	7	8	4	3
4	6	5	9	3	8	2	1	7
9	4	8	3	2	6	5	7	1
1	5	6	8	7	9	3	2	4
3	7	2	1	5	4	6	9	8

481.

8	7	2	3	9	5	1	6	4
4	9	1	7	6	2	5	3	8
6	5	3	8	4	1	7	2	9
2	3	4	6	8	7	9	1	5
1	8	7	9	5	3	2	4	6
9	6	5	2	1	4	3	8	7
3	4	8	5	2	9	6	7	1
5	2	6	1	7	8	4	9	3
7	1	9	4	3	6	8	5	2

482.

3	5	7	4	2	6	8	1	9
6	9	2	7	1	8	3	5	4
8	4	1	3	5	9	2	7	6
5	7	3	2	6	4	1	9	8
1	2	6	9	8	7	5	4	3
4	8	9	1	3	5	7	6	2
7	1	8	6	4	3	9	2	5
2	6	5	8	9	1	4	3	7
9	3	4	5	7	2	6	8	1

483.

1	8	4	7	2	5	3	9	6
3	9	2	6	8	1	4	7	5
5	7	6	3	4	9	1	2	8
2	5	8	1	3	6	9	4	7
9	4	3	8	5	7	2	6	1
7	6	1	2	9	4	5	8	3
4	3	7	9	1	8	6	5	2
6	1	5	4	7	2	8	3	9
8	2	9	5	6	3	7	1	4

484.

1	3	5	9	7	8	2	6	4
4	9	6	5	1	2	7	3	8
8	2	7	4	3	6	5	1	9
7	8	1	3	2	9	6	4	5
3	5	4	1	6	7	9	8	2
9	6	2	8	5	4	1	7	3
5	4	8	7	9	1	3	2	6
2	7	3	6	4	5	8	9	1
6	1	9	2	8	3	4	5	7

485.

6	4	8	1	7	5	3	2	9
1	2	7	9	8	3	4	6	5
9	3	5	2	4	6	1	7	8
3	9	4	8	6	2	7	5	1
8	1	6	7	5	4	9	3	2
5	7	2	3	1	9	8	4	6
2	8	9	5	3	7	6	1	4
7	6	1	4	2	8	5	9	3
4	5	3	6	9	1	2	8	7

486.

8	5	9	7	6	2	3	1	4
7	3	1	8	5	4	6	9	2
6	4	2	3	9	1	5	8	7
3	6	8	2	4	5	1	7	9
1	7	4	9	8	3	2	6	5
9	2	5	6	1	7	8	4	3
4	1	6	5	2	9	7	3	8
5	9	7	1	3	8	4	2	6
2	8	3	4	7	6	9	5	1

Solutions

487.

8	7	2	3	9	4	1	5	6
4	3	5	7	6	1	2	9	8
1	9	6	5	2	8	4	3	7
5	8	1	4	7	2	9	6	3
3	6	7	8	1	9	5	2	4
9	2	4	6	5	3	8	7	1
6	4	8	2	3	5	7	1	9
7	5	9	1	8	6	3	4	2
2	1	3	9	4	7	6	8	5

488.

6	5	1	9	2	7	3	8	4
2	4	8	6	3	1	5	9	7
7	9	3	8	5	4	6	2	1
5	3	6	4	1	8	2	7	9
9	8	2	3	7	6	1	4	5
4	1	7	5	9	2	8	6	3
3	2	4	1	6	9	7	5	8
1	7	9	2	8	5	4	3	6
8	6	5	7	4	3	9	1	2

489.

9	2	3	6	7	5	8	1	4
5	8	1	3	2	4	7	9	6
7	4	6	1	8	9	3	5	2
8	3	9	2	1	7	6	4	5
6	1	2	5	4	8	9	7	3
4	5	7	9	6	3	2	8	1
3	9	4	8	5	2	1	6	7
1	7	8	4	3	6	5	2	9
2	6	5	7	9	1	4	3	8

490.

8	2	5	4	3	9	7	1	6
9	7	3	1	6	2	4	5	8
6	1	4	8	5	7	3	9	2
5	3	1	7	8	6	9	2	4
7	6	2	9	4	5	1	8	3
4	9	8	3	2	1	5	6	7
1	8	6	5	7	3	2	4	9
3	4	9	2	1	8	6	7	5
2	5	7	6	9	4	8	3	1